MORE PRAISE FOR BOLD MOVES

"Jump is both a powerful and fun novel that will inspire you to transformative action. It provides clarity and important insight that helps me manage in today's chaotic world!"

—Chris Lloyd, Chief Operating Officer
Hermann Memorial Hospital

"Those who wish to make bold moves in their lives will find this book to be an indispensable travel companion."

—Bill Cleaver, Former Chairman
Howard Johnson International Operator's Council

"FANTASTIC! This powerful book enables readers to engage in multiple personal coaching sessions from the comfort of their arm chair. This is a must read for coaches and anyone interested in going to the next level of their professional or personal contribution."

—Karen Kimsey House, Founder and President
The Coaches Training Institute

"I have always dreamt of attaining my Optimal Operating State but never had the time or way to get there. *Bold Moves* is a simple and effective tool that creates the path for greater success in your live."

—Rick Albiero, President and CEO
TeleCommuting Advantage Group

"A wonderful book and, in fact, a blueprint for people who yearn to make the bold moves that will uncover and fulfill their dreams."

—Rob Klapper, Chief Marketing Officer
21st Century Insurance

MORE PRAISE FOR BOLD MOVES

"In my 33 years in the education and training industry I have explored, to help myself and others, numerous books focusing on how to move your personal and professional life forward. This book is among the best. The main character, "Jump" takes a fun, thought-provoking journey, transforming himself and achieving his dreams. You will be immediately engaged and inspired to make Bold Moves!!!

—Cynthia M. Payne, Corporate Director of Cultural Development, Isle of Capri Casinos, Inc.

"*Bold Moves* provides practical, actionable information on what has until now always been an abstract subject--namely, creating a life and a career that are inspired and purposeful. So many people want to do this, but simply have not had the tools or direction to make it so until now with this book."

—Molly Davis, Partner
Rainmaker Communications

"As a recent adult graduate from college and a single mother, this book helped me jump to my next bold move and is an awesome guide to help anyone make their dreams become their reality. The step-by-step process helped me identify my next goal and design a plan for making it happen. This is a wonderful novel that can help facilitate personal transformation."

—Monica Maxfield, Young Adult

"*Bold Moves* is a delightful book. The methods used to bring about transformation are nothing short of brilliant. I have read many inspirational titles in the capacity of my job and few have delivered a more memorable read. This book will be hugely inspirational and helpful to a great many people."

—Stephanie Rose Bird, Professional Editor

HERE'S TO YOUR
NEXT BOLD MOVE!

BOLD MOVES

JUMP
To Outstanding
Self-Managed Action

ALLAN MILHAM
SHAYLA ROBERTS

Pond Productions Publishing

Published in Phoenix, Arizona, by Pond Productions Publishing.
For information, address Pond Productions, LLC, 8912 East Pinnacle Peak Road, #631, Scottsdale, Arizona 85255.

FIRST EDITION

Designed by Shayla Roberts

Library of Congress Cataloguing-in-Publication Data has been requested.

ISBN 0-9786037-0-2

TO ALL THOSE

who have contributed
to humankind
by deliberately making
Bold Moves

and to those
who are now ready
to explore
Bold Move country.

We are delighted to be writing this preface to *Bold Moves – Jump to Outstanding Self-Managed Action* because it means that after three years of market research, creative collaboration and reader testing, the writing is complete and the book is going to press.

Unlike any other book we know about, *Bold Moves* is actually three works woven together: a novel about a visionary CEO who commits his company to individual transformation and global sustainability; a fable about a young frog named Jump who shows us why the imaginative kid-like part of each of us is vital to our capacity for courageous and correct action; and an operating manual we call the *Reader's Log* that isolates key points of the *J-U-M-P—Bold Moves* formula for use in developing an *Optimal Operating State*—or way of being—that brings ease and grace to the work of life.

Some of our early readers reminded us that the complexity of three books in one runs counter to best-selling-book-market conventional wisdom which essentially cautions, *keep it simple.* More than one reader said the principles in our book are important and deserve to be delivered in a "serious" non-fiction book, like Stephen Covey's *Seven Habits of Highly Successful People.* We thank them for recognizing our book's value, and for favorably comparing the validity of our talking points to the power of one of the greatest self-management books of all times. Our concern, however, has been that non-fiction self-help books primarily speak intellectually—to the mind, conveying information about how it can engage to successfully manage one's actions in the outer world. Our book begins by stressing that truly bold action is always preceded by skillful management of internal thoughts and feelings. So it was important to us to write to the heart and spirit as well and we thought that fable and fiction were the right forms for doing so.

Some readers loved our fable about Jump the frog and urged us to publish it alone in the tradition of Dr. Spencer Johnson's classic *Who Moved My Cheese.* Again, we are honored by the comparison to a marvelous work and glad that others seem charmed by our playful amphibians in the marsh. But our marsh is an intuitive place and can be disorienting to some of the readers who might benefit most from the *J-U-M-P* formula. So we included the *Reader's Log* talking points along with a more familiar, human cast of characters.

Finally, there were readers who best liked the business novel aspect of the book because it models how the private musings and moves of the personal growth process show up and play out in a corporate setting. We applaud these readers for possessing acute powers of self-reflection.

The majority of our readers responded with excitement to our three-books-in-one, expressing delight over the way we wove the different components together. Perhaps this is an affect of our thirty-second-sound-byte, multi-tasking culture where one's attention is expected to bounce from one landscape to another. The bottom line for us as authors is that we are flattered that so many responded by suggesting that we have written a possible best-seller. But in the end, that is not why we wrote our book.

For over fifteen years, Allan has worked with top performers in dozens of industries from start-ups to Fortune 50 companies, navigating them to more meaningful work and increasing their impact as leaders in their lives. This book began with his excitement about the value his work was having for his clients, and a desire to make it available to a wider audience.

Shayla came on board as a writer specializing in personal growth content and we soon identified three key insights we had discovered independently as professionals: that human development is a very complex matter; that it forces us beyond black and white thinking and into a nuanced rainbow of considerations and processes; and that it demands that we exercise and integrate the wisdom of the heart and spirit along with the knowledge of the mind.

So we wrote a playful, yet "serious," book for readers eager to embrace a little complexity in order to limit doubts and fears and open to new dimensions of their destiny. Some will find them in the business novel. Some will sense them in the marsh fable. Others will skim the highlights through our talking points. But we suggest that it may be the very process of moving between the dimensions of the book that awakens the undiscovered aspects of self that will ultimately realize those new dimensions of destiny.

We hope you enjoy the journey.

Allan Milham and Shayla Roberts

CONTENTS

ONE

Global Thrills, Inc. Corporate Headquarters, Los Angeles, CA

A glaring ray of sunshine falls across the special interest page of Ernest Cottingham's morning paper, highlighting a modestly sized headline. He lets it pass without notice apart from the involuntary flicker of his pupils in response to the morning sun's glare. Ernest is absorbed. Each day, he reads the financial section cover to cover, scanning the sport and political commentary pages, leaving the rest of the paper on the seat of the limousine that takes him to work. Though he is interested in a broad range of subjects, to Ernest, the special interest pages of *The Times* are mostly fluff—raw material for the papier-mâché animals his nine-year-old grandson enjoys making.

The sun persists. "Read this," it demands, flashing between tall buildings as the limo approaches downtown Los Angeles. The reader's glance is captured, his interest drawn. *Well I'll be darned*, Ernest says to himself, *there's a surprisingly 'spin-free' statement: Frogs Are Dying Worldwide.* He reads on:

> Some 5,000 species of amphibians inhabit the world, mostly frogs, toads, and salamanders. Scientists are concerned because the number of living amphibians is dwindling dramatically each year. A substantial decline in eggs that survive to tadpole stage is noted, along with an escalating rate of birth defects. Millions of tadpoles, young frogs and toads are genetically disabled,

> making them easy prey for natural predators.
>
> Amphibians have inhabited the blue planet for 350 million years, surviving the massive extinction that followed the dinosaur age. Their sudden decline suggests that danger to natural systems on a global scale may be reaching levels that threaten humans as well.
>
> Frogs and toads may be the twenty-first century's version of the proverbial canary in the mineshaft. Canaries were once used as sentinels. When the bird died, miners left the mine because they knew toxic gases were reaching lethal levels. The problem for humans in the case of dying frog's stems from the fact that we don't know what's causing the deaths, and unlike those miners, we have nowhere else to go.

Ernest Cottingham is founder and CEO of Global Thrills, Inc., one of the hottest family entertainment stocks on the market. He is also a particularly astute and imaginative student of global systems and their effects upon one another. He understands how subtle changes in one domain, like economics for example, can create huge consequences for another, like politics.

Ernest follows chaos theory. He knows the forces of nature always affect every aspect of life, even business. Events in recent years have proven that a single tidal wave or hurricane could permanently alter the face of a vast region, affecting commerce on a global scale. The article on frogs reminds Ernest of dire implications he knows all too well. The dwindling number of frogs directly impacts life on Earth.

Life matters to Ernest. It matters very much. To put it simply, in his mind, vibrant, sustainable life on Earth is good for business. Period. Without it, he sees no need for goods and services and—obviously—no resources from which to produce them. That is not the kind of legacy he wants to leave his grandson, Ernie. No. Ernest is committed to creating a different outcome. He dreams of a world where the bottom line requirements of present day multinational corporations can be achieved without compromising the social vitality of future generations and the ecological health of planet Earth.

He reflects upon the gargantuan effort required to create his desired outcome, and is reminded of another frog story; the old tale of the frog that is dropped into a pot of boiling water and jumps out again in a reflexive action that saves him from becoming frog stew. As the story goes, a second frog is put into a pot of cool water and swims about happily while the stove heats up. Because the change in temperature is gradual, this second frog doesn't notice he is in danger until it is too late. *That's how we humans are*, Ernest is thinking. We*'re swimming around oblivious to the fact that our world is about to make stew of us.*

As his limo pulls to the curb, he ponders the plight of amphibians and is struck with an insight. I've always assumed that the great question of our time is something like, "How do we get the frog in the pot to notice that the temperature is rising before it's too late?" But, what if the frog is so excited about life that he just wants out of the pot so he can get on with what he's doing? What if he's bored with swimming in circles? What if he finds passion in the very act of jumping? What if the great question of our time is really, "How do we help the frog jump out of the pot for his own good reasons before the water temperature nears the boiling point?"

Setting *The Times* on the seat next to him, Ernest sees a

small ad beneath the article on frogs:

JUMP
Making Bold Moves in an Uncertain World
Coaching and Consulting Services
The life you save may be your own!

Tearing the ad from the page, he stuffs it into the side pocket of his briefcase and makes the call moments later from his desk on the 50th floor of the Citicorp building.

"Joe Putnam here," says the voice on the line. "How can I help you?"

"I'm not really sure," says Cottingham. "I read your ad in this morning's paper. And well, the ad paralleled what I had been thinking just seconds before."

"Hmm," says Putnam, "a meaningful coincidence. They always intrigue me too. May I ask what it was in particular that caught your attention?"

"The word 'jump'," says Ernest. "This probably sounds a little crazy, but I was thinking about how we've got to be able to get excited about jumping—jumping out of the status quo. Jumping into action driven by passion."

"You're talking about what I call making Bold Moves," says Putnam. "I do understand, and perhaps I can help. Let's schedule a time to talk in more depth."

The following Thursday, after what can only be described as a rigorous phone interview—not by Ernest, but of Ernest—Mr. Putnam seems satisfied that Cottingham is likely to be a viable Bold Moves coaching client.

The interview process is a mind-bender for Ernest. Not since his first job search out of college, has he been willing to subject himself to the level of scrutiny that Mr. Putnam brings to bear. As a powerful CEO, Ernest expects to ask the questions, not answer them. He expects to make the judgment calls, not be subjected to them. But Putnam is extremely clear and very compelling, and Ernest is definitely intrigued. This guy has the confidence to hold my feet to the fire, he thinks to himself.

"The first thing we must do," says Putnam, "is clearly define the outcomes you desire from our work together. We have identified that you are already a Bold Moves maker in your own right, what we might call a 'natural.' As I understand it, you want to gain more conscious awareness about the intelligence you bring to making Bold Moves so that you can begin sharing it with others in your organization. Is that right?"

"Exactly," says Ernest. "I want to identify the Bold Move makers in my company and expand their reach and influence. I want to mentor them into developing a Bold Moves culture at Global Thrills, Inc. I believe we can become a microcosm for the kind of courageous, principled action that is needed in the business world—action that fosters profitable commerce, but also reverses the decline that's occurring in our great natural systems."

The phone is hot in his hands as Ernest feels the excitement of his vision for corporate—and global—transformation. "As far as I'm concerned," he says, "the current state of affairs results from an acute lack of imagination. Those of us who have the power have gotten fat and lazy. Unless we start using our influence responsibly and creatively, our legacy will be a massive decline in the quality of all life on Earth."

"Love the passion in your voice," says Putnam. "Let's get started."

There's a soft throat clearing sound on the phone as Putnam collects his thoughts. "Your first assignment is to begin reading a little book I'll send you. It's a fable. About frogs."

"Another meaningful coincidence?" says Cottingham.

"In more ways than one," says Putnam. "The book is called Jump. It's an easy read, and will provide your quickest exposure to the basics of Bold Moves making. You'll have to set your critical mind aside, though, to receive full value from the story. Are you open to doing that?"

"Sure," says Ernest, wondering *what's the big deal? I've read a number of business fables.* "I'll try to keep an open mind."

"And one more thing," says Putnam, "it will be important to our work that you take notes as you read, to capture your thoughts and, dare I say 'feelings' about the story."

"All right, sure," says Cottingham. "Where do I find this fable? I want to get started right away."

"I'll send you a copy along with a notebook. The drill to begin with is for you to notice, as you read, whenever your mind begins to close. Use the notebook to record any judgments that arise.

"Oh, and Ernest, it seems very reasonable to me that you may find more than one Bold Move maker in the ranks of a company with a name like Global Thrills, Inc."

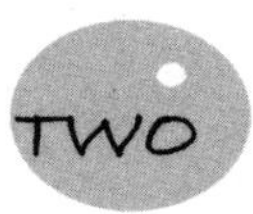

Global Thrills Family Arena, Kalamazoo, Michigan

Evelyn Dodd is general manager for Global's oldest, most successful family entertainment arena. Maintaining first place status among twenty arenas worldwide, she's into competition as steep as an Alpine slope. Global loves Evelyn Dodd because Evelyn found, signed and debuted the company's hottest international commodity; Jackson U. McPlayer.

She did it quietly, right here in Kalamazoo, under the radar of corporate. She did it with stealth, billing McPlayer as a warm up act at first, and then gaining courage as he found his following. What a coup. What an act—a Harley riding phenomenon! *His caravan arrives on Friday,* she's thinking, *and ticket sales are off the chart for the weekend. I'm even getting calls from Global board members requesting special passes.*

THREE

Global Thrills Family Arena, Austin, Texas

Landing hard on his custom chromed front wheel, Jackson Ulysses McPlayer revs his Harley engine for the matinee crowd before somersaulting onto the handlebars for his final sixty-mile an hour bow. Twenty five thousand fans roar back their appreciation for the show's finale, a death defying leap through seven rings of fire, each strategically positioned in a giant arc across the arena. Sleek in red lycra, Jackson's muscles bulge like a fighting man's. Surfing on adrenalin as he always does at this point in the show, Jackson revels in the exciting life he lives as an icon in the world of daredevil entertainment.

Later, in a more pensive mood, he ponders a computer animation of the new addition to his act. In weeks to come, he will perform it at Evelyn Dodd's arena in Kalamazoo. There are several software programs to tweak and some rehearsals to cram into his schedule to make ready. *Oh, but it will be worth it,* he's thinking.

FOUR

Global Thrills Corporate Headquarters, Los Angeles, CA

A sawing sound echoes through Ernest's office as he pulls the rip tab, opening an express package that has just arrived. Two items are removed and inspected: the promised book, *Bold Move - Jump to Outstanding Self-Managed Action*, and a notebook, blank except for the title *Reader's Log*. Checking his watch, he finds a few minutes to spare before his lunch appointment. Ernest eagerly opens to the first chapter, and begins reading.

> The Fogg Family was a clan of nighttime frogs living in Metro Marsh, just minutes by bird from the heart of Atlanta. For thousands of generations dating back to before the age of dinosaurs, it had been the Fogg family's responsibility to gather just at dusk and awaken the other nighttime creatures of the marsh.
>
> Dermand and Skita Fogg were the parents of three tadpoles named after the noise making jobs they would one day perform; Plop, Croak and Jump. Plop and Croak were looking forward to the roles they were to play in life, but try as he might, Jump simply could not get excited about the work laid out before him. It wasn't just that his legs were taking forever to form; his tail was strong and so was his voice, and he had every reason to believe his legs would be too in time, but he sensed he had a greater purpose—a calling beyond the marsh.
>
> Each morning Dermand and Skita tucked the tadpoles into their waterbeds and urged them to

dream in shades of marshland gray. One day, a very strange thing happened. As he slept, Jump did not dream in shades of gray. He dreamed he was jumping from red leaf to yellow on long legs of bright emerald green. When he woke at dusk, he couldn't wait to tell Plop and Croak about his dream. As he shared his story, it scared them a little. They told him to mind the marsh and imagine himself jumping from gray leaf to gray as he'd been told.

The next day, it happened again. Jump dreamed in vivid color only this time he wore a raspberry red frog suit with *Star Dude* written on the front in dazzling rhinestones. Waking a few minutes before full dusk even more excited than before, he decided not to ruin his mood by relating the dream to his siblings. Instead, he swam to where Dermand and Skita sat on a log, warming up for their night duties. They listened carefully to what Jump had to say, and well, they were flabbergasted. No Fogg family member had ever dreamed such dreams—*surely something was very, very wrong*. They told him he should try harder to dream in shades of marshland gray. "Visualize yourself jumping from leaf to leaf in the deepest, blackest night," they said.

When dawn came again and Jump fell asleep, his rainbow world grew larger. He dreamed he wore the raspberry red Star Dude suit in an international leaping competition and won a shocking blue ribbon when his emerald green legs leaped him through a flaming orange hoop! On hearing this, Skita Fogg felt a tear form in one of her giant frogeyes and she worried. *How will Jump ever be happy in the grays and darks of the nighttime marsh with such vivid, exciting dreams?*

Ernest puts the little book down. *It is an easy read,* he's thinking, *too easy. I'm not sure it will hold my attention. I want answers, not fairy tales.* His eyes fall to the notebook and he records his thoughts.

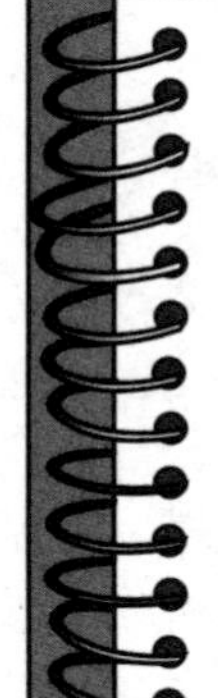

I'm having a hard time reading this story.

It seems too simple.

Where's the meat?

"Good," says Putnam during their phone session later that afternoon, "that's just the kind of self-reflection I was hoping you would do. Now let's talk about why this fairy tale might be important in getting to your objective of gaining conscious awareness about how you've accomplished the Bold Moves you've made in life.

"Do you remember when I first interviewed you, how frustrated you were with the lack of imagination in corporate leadership?"

"Yes," says Ernest, "it drives me crazy that leaders can't think past the numbers on their stock reports."

"Here's the point," says Putnam. "Imagination is fueled by intuition. The two are so closely associated in the human psyche, that most people, including many hard driving business people, believe that intuition is imaginary. And what is the commonly held belief about imagination?"

"That's tricky," says Ernest, "because on the one hand, people who understand innovation know that it begins with imagination; on the other hand, they are likely to be extremely critical of imaginative ideas, especially their own."

"Is that true of you?" asks Putnam. "Do you criticize your own imaginative thoughts?"

"Not really. In fact, I think I thrive on new ideas. They are the excitement in my life."

"So there's your first clue," says Putnam, "about why you are different, and why Bold Moves are natural for you. Bold Moves begin with an openness to intuitive insight and new, imaginative ideas."

"So the excitement that's needed to have the frog jumping out of the pot for his own good reasons begins with intuition and imagination," says Ernest. "That makes sense, but what does it have to do with reading this book?"

"Your knee jerk reaction to the book is much like the reaction people have to their own imagination," says Putnam. "It seems to be too simple, even childish, so the busy grown up CEO judges it as being irrelevant and sets it aside without due consideration. The problem with that is that the ability to access intuition and imagination is directly linked to the ability to contact the little kid inside the busy exec."

These words strike a cord for Ernest. As far as he knows, there are only a handful of business leaders who have the foresight and imagination to truly comprehend the degree to which multinational corporations are poised on the balance beam in the twenty-first century. On one side is the threat of mass extinction of an untold number of species. On the other side is the possibility of outrageous, innovative sustainability. Every one of those leaders is creative and open-minded, much like a child. Believing in their ability to envision creative solutions, they have studied global phenomena in depth and they realize how the massive power of transnational business interests will, inevitably, tip the balance one way or the other.

Ernest and his associates are committed to the possibility of the balance tipping in the direction of sustaining—and even proliferating—vitality and diversity in Earth's complex living systems. They have empathy for people who prefer not to expose themselves to the concerns that have become, for these few, a personal quest. The facts are daunting, and once seriously considered, they become all consuming.

Taking part in an international think tank, Cottingham has been shaken, even tearful at times, as graphic presentations give witness to the collapse of life on Earth as he has known it. He feels desperate to get the word out—to make more broadly known what he knows, so that more can be done. He understands, though, that it's a very tricky proposition to bring such hard facts before the public. *With devastation spreading at a rate that could exterminate frogs and who knows what other species in my lifetime,* he wonders, *how are we to wake up in time?*

Based on his commitment to change the end of the story for his grandson and for all other creatures on Earth, Ernest has laid groundwork inside Global Thrills, Inc., adopting a management style that promotes ethics and accountability. He is a principled leader, one of the best of a good lot that is committed not only to excellent financial returns for investment dollars, but to excellence in human resource management and in win-win business relationships. Ernest and his associates initiate within their growth plans, community involvement and environmental protection. They intuit and institute measures to support their principles and practices, and they maintain connections to a network of resources that help them. Having come to grips with the facts before them, and having taken bold measures to address those facts within their own companies, Ernest and his associates are primed for the next steps. *Now, we have to ramp up our ability to innovate and extend our influence into broader realms.*

"I think I see what you mean," he says to Putnam. "To gain a deeper understanding of the business of Bold Moves, I need to become conscious about my relationship with the creative part of me, the kid, and you're saying that reading the Jump book is a way to do that."

"That's exactly right," says Joe. "If you want to mentor others in the business of Bold Moves, you'll need to help them access their imagination and intuition. You've got to get it in your own bones first."

"Give me a minute, will you?" says Ernest. "I want to write down something you said before." Opening his Reader's Log, he writes:

Bold Moves begin with a mind that's open to intuitive insight and new, imaginative ideas.

These reside in the domain of the creative little kid part of you.

"I suspect from what you're saying," he says to Putnam, "that the content of the book might not be as simple as it first appears."

"True, true," Joe replies in a quality of voice that implies understatement. "As you know, there is no such thing as a quick fix in business—nor in addressing environmental issues. Well, there are no overnight successes in the Bold Moves business, either. To use my analogy about the creative little kid, one of the reasons why intuition and imagination are trained out of children is because those qualities are complex by nature. Most authority figures like teachers, parents, and even bosses, don't know how to handle complexity when it shows up in a person's behavior. They often don't even know how to define intuition and imagination in practical terms. First, they require skill development and expanded awareness."

"Yes," says Ernest. "I can see that I'm going to have to work on those things myself. Okay, I'll give the book another try."

"Might I suggest that you read it someplace other than at your office? If you're like most adults, your subconscious mind has had very good reasons over the years for leaving some aspects of your internal little kid in a safe place, away from the pressures of work. Maybe you could access him more readily in a place that evokes creativity and possibility for you."

"That's a great idea," Ernest replies, "and you're right, you know, my imagination seems to work best away from the office. In fact, I get great ideas in the shower. I've learned to write them down and take them to work with me."

FIVE

Cottingham Estate,
Westwood, CA

Nine-year-old Ernie Cottingham tumbles into the great room where his grandfather has just clicked off the TV. “Look at this one,” he says proudly, exhibiting one of his paper creations. “It’s a *velociraptor*. His legs are kinda wobbly so I propped him up a little, but look at his claws! I made ‘em out of pop tops.”

Ernest is once again captivated by one of the boy’s uniquely detailed papier-mâché animals. “It’s great,” he says. And then, for no reason he can explain in the moment, he continues, “Did you know that your raptor there was predated by frogs?”

“What is predated?” Ernie asks.

“It means that something came before something else, like that frogs existed on Earth even before dinosaurs.”

“I thought dinosaurs were about the oldest living things,” says Ernie.

“No,” says Ernest. “Frogs, toads and salamanders are just some of the animals that have been on Earth longer. Many other species predated dinosaurs, but most have since become extinct.”

“How come you know so much about frogs?” asks Ernie.

“Well, I’ve been studying frogs a bit. In fact, I have some homework here,” says Ernest, tapping on a book in his lap, “to read about frogs.”

“Can I listen?” asks Ernie.

Ernest chuckles. He is surprised as always by his grandson’s way of looking at things. “I hadn’t thought about reading it out loud,” he says, “but why not? Let’s give it a try. Find yourself a place on the sofa here and I'll fill you in on the first part of the story."

Ernest tells Ernie about the pond and the frog family; and about how Jump is supposed to dream in gray and black, but can't help dreaming in bright colors. Then he reads aloud.

> On seeing Skita's tears in response to Jump's dream, Dermand puzzled a moment. "Hoops," he said, "I've heard of hoops. Uncle Faddiest Tode has hoops. Maybe you should go talk to him. You'll have to wake early, though, because Faddiest is a daytime toad. He seldom stirs after the sun goes down."

"I need to make a note, here," Ernest says to Ernie. "Hold on for just a second." Reaching for the Reader's Log, he scrawls out:

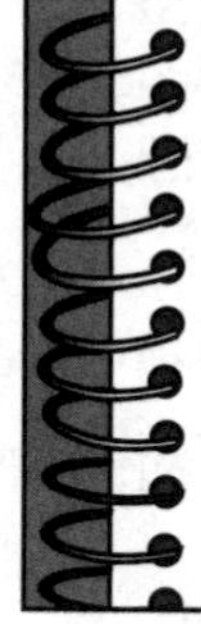

There are places in our lives
where we're not meant
to go alone.

Seek out support.

Ernie's upturned hands and lifted eyebrows express his impatience with the interruption.

"It's part of my homework," Ernest says. "I should have told you I'd have to stop now and then to write some things down. Are we cool?"

Ernie nods and Ernest reads on.

> That morning, when Jump went down to his

waterbed, he yanked on the long, skinny leg of a crested spoonbill that happened to be standing nearby. "Would you wake me," he asked the bird, "twenty minutes before dusk?"

At precisely the moment requested, the slurping sounds of the spoonbill whisked past Jump's ear membranes and his eyes opened up to glistening sunlight rippling across marsh water in late afternoon. "Like rhinestones," he said to himself. Swimming off in search of Uncle Faddiest, he spotted the old toad on dry land not far from the water's edge.

Faddiest Tode's body was taut and trim like that of a much younger toad. The only evidence of his ancient age was a universe of wisdom warts that covered every inch of skin. His personal world was like an odd museum you might find tucked away on a big city side street, filled with fanciful items gathered over many years for mysterious reasons. Jump spied the hoops that Dermand had mentioned—seven hula hoops actually—standing upright between two trees, with a label that read "1950s". Other spaces held a myriad of other objects: baseball cards, Dilbert™ coffee mugs, Pet Rocks, iMac™ T-shirts, Barbie® Dolls, Beanie Babies™, and other diverse things, all carefully stowed and labeled.

Faddiest himself was stomping purposefully about, breaking in a retro pair of shoes he'd won on E-Bay®; but he stopped in his tracks when Jump approached—as though he knew without being told, that someone was approaching with a question. Answering before he was asked, he said, "You can have anything you want." Then, he sprang nimbly into a nearby thicket.

"Wait," said Jump, "I need to know about emerald green and raspberry red, and sparkling rhinestones . .

. . and flaming orange hoops."

Faddiest squinted through the brush in Jump's direction. It was a little late for a coaching session, but he sensed it was important and thought, *after all, how often has one of my Fogg kin asked about the world of vivid color?*

"What's your name then, youngster?" Tode called out, unseen.

"Jump. My name is Jump."

"Good," called Tode, "that's a very good name. Do you know its meaning?"

"Well, yes," said Jump. "It's the name of the job I'm to have when I grow up. I'll jump about just as the sun goes down, helping to wake the nighttime creatures of the marsh."

Tode's head popped out from the thicket wearing a curious look. "Then what's this about emerald green, raspberry red and flaming orange hoops?" he asked.

"My dreams," answered Jump. "The colors come in my dreams and I can't make them go away. First I dreamed of myself jumping with emerald green legs on red and yellow leaves. Then I dreamed I wore a raspberry red Star Dude suit and won a bright blue ribbon for jumping through a flaming orange hoop!"

"Oh my," said Tode, "those are colorful dreams indeed! I can see how they might set you to questioning a future bound up in shades of nighttime gray."

"But I am a nighttime frog," said Jump. "Aren't I? Isn't it my fate to jump about in shades of gray?"

Tode came closer. "Your name Jump may prove to have more than one meaning," he said peering down into the water where Jump's tadpole shape swayed gently back and forth. *He's strong*, Tode thought to himself. *He will be a jumper all right.*

"Your dreams are trying to tell you that jumping

is, indeed, a big part of your future," he said.

Lights in the tadpole's tiny eyes glistened with expectation until the little guy couldn't hold in his question one more second. "Can I learn to jump in the world of colors?"

Tode's wisdom warts shivered deep into his thick skin. He was a coach, a very good one, with many years of experience. In the course of helping important, powerful creatures grow and change, he had proven to himself again and again, that anyone could dramatically alter their direction in life by making what he called Bold Moves.

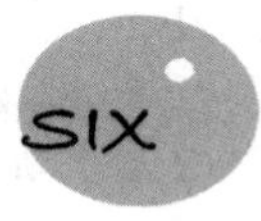

SIX

Global Thrills, Inc. Corporate Headquarters, Los Angeles, CA

Joe Putnam's voice comes through the speakerphone on Ernest's desk. "It sounds to me," he says, "that you're saying you want to innovate even further in your management style."

"I believe that is correct," Ernest answers. "I trust my people to perform for the company, but if I'm serious about 'getting the frog to jump out of the pot for his own reasons,' I want to find those frogs who are capable of jumping and help them identify their reasons for doing so. And I need to support those frogs in mentoring others towards making Bold Moves."

"That's a radical notion," Joe replies, reflecting the conflicted tone in Ernest's voice.

"It's completely counter-intuitive," Ernest answers. "We've already flattened the pyramid at Global Thrills. Now I'm considering turning it upside-down. Asking people to bring their personal passions with them to work is a dangerous proposition, but if I'm reading the *Jump* book correctly, passionate dreams and visions are drivers in the Bold Move conversation. Passion for the world of color is what prompts Jump to explore beyond the nighttime marsh. And passion, rather than fear, I suppose, is what motivates the frog to leap out of the pot while the water's at a moderate temperature. Still, if I move on this, it could create chaos in the ranks."

Putnam presses, saying, "For weeks, you've been asserting that we are all headed for chaos on a global scale if you and your associates don't take bold, innovative action. You also identified that the place where you are the most influential at present, is right inside your own company."

"True," Ernest concurs. "I'm just not sure how to begin."

"I submit that you already have," Joe reminds him. "You've seeded a culture that is ripe for Bold Moves; and you're gaining new understanding about how and why you yourself have been motivated to make Bold Moves. Ultimately, one so-called 'frog' at a time, you can foster a community that helps you hold the chaos of the Bold Move conversion. Who can you think of in your company that is showing signs of Bold Move readiness?"

Cottingham reflects on the question after the coaching call. There must be someone, he's thinking, someone in Global who thinks independently; someone who's already running their own show on some level; someone whose personal desires authentically align with those of the organization, but who knows how to successfully forward original ideas.

Ernest knows he isn't starting from scratch. The notion of alignment of personal values to the objectives of Global's corporate authority has been fostered for a number of years as part of the company's forward thinking, culture building initiative—now to add the element of personal passion into the mix. *The stage is properly set and it's a good thing. We're running out of time.*

On his desk is the most recent update from the network on global sustainability:

Water, the precious element that makes up seventy percent of the human body and covers seventy percent of Earth's surface, is running afoul worldwide.

Great aquifers are being drained far beyond their ability to replenish. This creates empty fissures and caverns that collapse, closing the natural vessels that once held reserves.

The oceans are polluted and threatening the demise of the relatively modest percentage of food fish that still survive. Dead zones lurk beneath the surface of thousands of square miles of oceans, lakes and rivers.

Hidden beneath major metropolitan areas are vast

plumes of toxic industrial waste, seeping into what remains of diminishing supplies of local potable water in aquifers.

SEVEN

Cottingham Estate,
Westwood, CA

"I'm working on a new animal," says Ernie, settling in beside his grandfather for the next episode of the book. "It's a statue of Jump."

"What a great idea," says Ernest, removing the bookmark that shows their place. "I look forward to seeing that."

The reading continues.

> Tode had very specific ideas about what Bold Moves are and what they are not. He was distinguished within the amphibian coaching profession for having defined the fundamental difference between Barely, Brash, and Bold Moves.
>
> He would say to clients, "Barely Moves are the favorite actions of creatures sometimes known as 'couch potatoes.' They move slowly, and only when it is absolutely necessary. Couch potatoes are passive in nature. They like to watch the moves made by others, especially the sports idols and other famous people on the TV. Barely Move makers don't give much attention to their own ideas and actions.
>
> "Then there are Brash Move makers, the creatures who seem to make moves that are bold, but which upon closer examination, prove to be merely brash. Brash Move makers get so caught up

in thoughts, beliefs and actions of others that they do things without thinking first. A Brash Move is like a patch that is put on a circumstance, a quick fix. The primary emotions that motivate Brash Moves are fear and doubt. Anyone can make a Brash Move at the drop of a shoe. Sometimes even couch potatoes will get excited enough—or angry enough—to make a Brash Move, but they often regret it. In fact, couch potatoes are known to use their bad experiences with Brash Move making as evidence that it is not safe to move at all.

"Some Brash Move makers are called 'movers and shakers.' These creatures are very assertive, even aggressive in nature, and tend to think that any idea they have is worth putting into action just because they thought of it. They almost never examine the long-term consequences of their moves, and they often make great big messes in the world that have to be cleaned up by others.

"Bold Move makers, on the other hand, are creatures who are purposeful and deliberate in what they do. They act based on guidance from their deepest inner truths. Bold Moves require preparation; exploration, research, and carefully planned execution. The emotions that motivate Bold Move makers are not fear and doubt, but hope and possibility. Bold Move makers penetrate the essence of a circumstance and then align themselves to that essence from the core of their authentic nature. They trust their ideas because they check them out, and the moves they make are often ingenious and highly beneficial. Bold

Move makers create successes both short and long term."

Ernest stops reading to make another note:

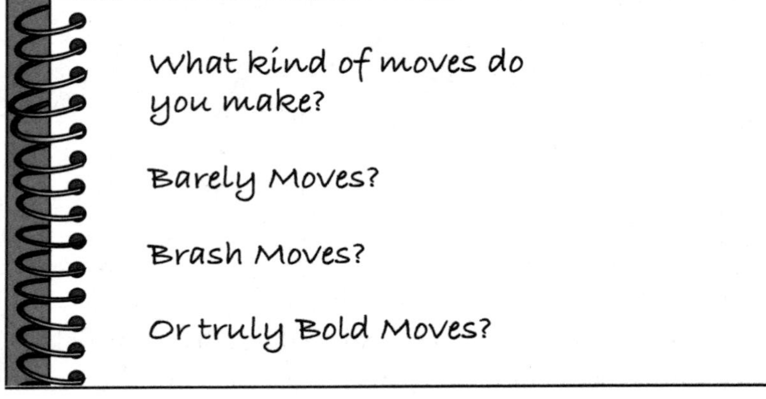

"Do you think I'm a Barely Mover because I watch TV?" Ernie asks.

"No," answers Ernest. "You balance your TV watching with other interests. In fact, I personally think that making your paper animals is a kind of Bold Move. You think carefully about what you're doing, and you do it because you know it's right for you."

"What are consequences?" the boy asks, referring to a word from the story.

"Something that follows as a result of a decision or an action."

"What does authentic mean?"

"It means something like the words genuine or true, combined with original or unique," says Ernest, realizing how adult focused this fairy tale truly is.

They read on.

Faddiest knew that one's readiness to explore was an essential prerequisite for approaching Bold Moves. He was very careful not to build false hope in those who came to him and were not yet ready. Having identified certain factors that needed to be in place, he interviewed prospective clients, assessing them for qualities like courage, determination, creativity and discipline.

Bold Move readiness is essential and must be carefully assessed.

This is what my coach Joe Putnam was doing when he interviewed me.

Naturally each individual had a unique combination of attributes, but there was one quality without which a creature simply could not approach making Bold Moves. That non-negotiable quality was a curious and open mind.

So it was in the spirit of respectful probing that Tode answered Jump's question—Can I learn to jump in the world of colors—with a question of his own.

"Are you open?" he asked.

"Open?" said Jump.

"Yes, open," said Tode. "We can't go forward unless we're certain that you're open—to new ideas and possibilities."

"What kind of possibilities?" said Jump.

"Well for one," answered Tode, "the possibility that your cup is always half full, and never half empty. So far, based on what you've been told and shown, you've seen the day as always just ending. Are you open to seeing the day as just beginning?"

Jumps eyes bulged to marble size, strained by the question; and then they retracted into small slits. "I don't know," he said.

"Then lets try another question," said Tode. "Are you open to the possibility of becoming a daytime frog instead of a nighttime frog?"

"I don't know," said Jump, again. "Do I have to decide right now?"

"Heavens no," said Tode. "A change like that is fundamental, truly on the order of a Bold Move. You don't have nearly enough experience or information to make such a move yet. If you're open to the possibility, though, you can take a next step by exploring the daytime world. That's where you'll find emerald green, raspberry red, and all the other colors of your dreams. Check them out. See if they appeal to you as much when you're awake as they do when you're asleep and dreaming."

"Wow," said Jump, starting to sense the excitement of the possibilities Uncle Faddiest offered.

Ernest takes a break again from the reading to record thoughts.

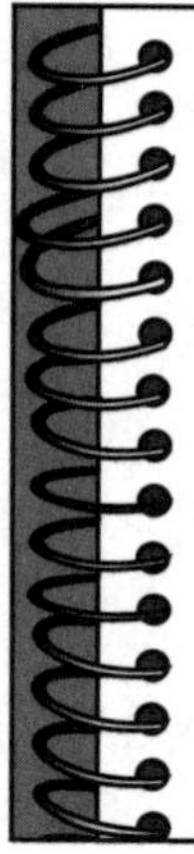

Are you open to possibilities?

Can you always see the world as "cup half full"

And see the day as just beginning instead of just ending?

Tode's wisdom warts took to dancing in celebration of Jump's enthusiasm. Smiling inside, he chuckled aloud, "We're going to need a proper coaching session. Let's set an appointment for first thing tomorrow. Can you stay awake until then?"

Caught up in anticipation over seeing more of the bright colors of his dreams, Jump blurted, "Yes!"

Just as quickly, a doubt clutched him and he added, "I mean, I don't think so!"

Faddiest's experienced eye recognized the struggle in Jump's brain. *This is a powerful coaching moment,* he thought to himself. *On the one hand, the tadpole's blurted, "yes," is refreshingly different from the guarded expressions that most of my very important adult clients can allow themselves, especially in our early sessions. Most have lost the art of permitting themselves enthusiastic outbursts, those positive body-based messages of the intuitive inner voice that tells a creature what it authentically wants and needs. Most adults of all species have long since silenced that important voice, but it is crucial to informing the process of making Bold Moves.*

On the other hand, he thought to himself, *Jump's rebound to 'I don't think so,' signals the presence of a more primitive, negative instinct voice, one of many that react out of doubt and fear.*

It was from his awareness of these different voices that Tode said to Jump, "'Yes' is a very good answer when you're exploring new territory. The Bold Moves business is founded on saying 'yes' to lots of new ideas and opportunities. I call the 'yes' voice The Whisperer. It rises up from inside you very softly at first, inviting you to act on what is important to you. The Whisperer is your positive voice of imaginative intuition talking."

> The Whisperer
>
> is the positive voice of possibility, the wisdom of imagination and intuition.
>
> Listen for The Whisperer.
>
> It is pro-active in nature.

Tode said to Jump, "It is also important to note, here, that your mind seemed to split into two different notions just now when your answers boomeranged from 'yes' to 'I don't think so.' The 'I don't think so' message is just one of many doubts that will fill your mind in the coming weeks, months, and even years, if you decide to delve more deeply into the business of Bold Moves. It will become important to hear the voices of doubt and fear as distinct in your ear. I call those voices Inner Critters. They pressure you to act out of doubt and fear."

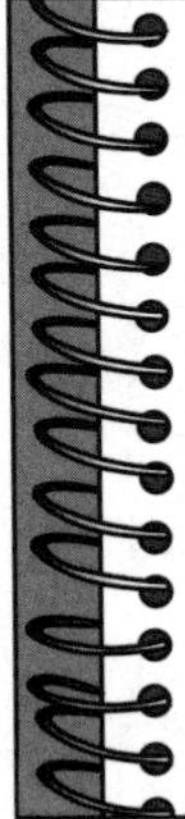

Inner Critters

are the negative voices
of instinctual doubt
and fear.

They are reactive in nature.

Watch for Inner Critters.

This is a lot of new information for a small tadpole, Tode thought to himself. *The light is waning in the marsh. It's time for Jump to mind his nighttime duties and for me to get some rest.*

"If you want to know more about making Bold Moves," he said, "I'll see you right here, first thing in the morning." Then he disappeared once again into the thicket.

Jump's mind was full to the brim as he pondered the idea of different kinds of voices in his head. It troubled him a little, especially when he began to hear more mixed messages bubbling up: *How will I ever stay awake past dawn? I should be awake at dawn. I'll try to be awake. I need to be awake. I'll never be awake!*

His conflicting thoughts wore him down before the moon came up. To keep from drifting off, he plopped and croaked and practiced kicking in the darkness even though his legs were only a latent impulse near the top of his tail. The burst of physical activity tired him even more until all he could do was swim off to his waterbed, hours before first light.

Deep in slumber, some part of Jump knew that he was sleeping at the wrong time. He dreamed of the world being upside-down and inside out. Then magically, as if from a far away dreamland place, his mind came full circle, back to the excitement he had felt earlier, and he heard a powerful voice within say once again, *Yes.* And then, *I simply will wake up at dawn.*

Focus your mind on what you intend.

Jump's intention:
I simply will wake up at dawn.

Ernest puts the bookmark between the pages of the Jump

book. "I think I hear The Whisperer talking to me," he says to Ernie with a grin, "and I need to spend some time just listening."

The boy nods, recognizing his grandfather's retreat into the world of adults. "See ya later," he says bounding off the sofa.

Ernest has determined that Global Thrills arena managers are his best targets in his hunt for the frog most ready to leap out of the pot. He has reviewed performance records and planned his search. Now his intuition—The Whisperer—tells him it's time to take action. Punching in his assistant's voice mail number, he leaves a message about his up-coming travel needs.

EIGHT

Global Thrills, Inc. Corporate Jet, Sydney, Australia

Cottingham is on the last leg of a trip taking him onsite to arenas around the globe to review his three top 'frog' candidates. So far, he has found no jumpers, only swimmers. Stopping first in Kyoto, Japan, he interviewed a very responsible, bottom line oriented arena manager, only to determine that the guy would likely follow Ernest right into Armageddon without offering a single original thought. His stop in Sydney netted only slightly better results. He found an energetic top performer who was visibly frustrated by the constraints he attributed to "corporate," but he lacked the courage and originality to offer viable alternatives.

Finding my frog is a lot more difficult than I thought it would be, Ernest thinks to himself as his private jet lifts off, heading back to the States. I was afraid that if I pulled back the mantle of corporate authority looking for individualists, all hell would break loose. It turns out that the mantle is cast from stubbornly held beliefs left over from the industrial age. Even my most courageous employees are seeking approval, if not outright direction, from above. It's no wonder so many innovators leave big companies and launch entrepreneurial ventures. It's what I'd do myself if I felt as hamstrung as these people feel. And we're the good guys! When compared to most companies, we bend over backwards to foster original thinking and independent action.

In his quest for the rare 'frog' who wants to jump for

reasons of his own, Ernest sees more clearly how many—if not most—reasonable adults are simply programmed to keep their thinking and their actions within what they deem to be 'safe' bounds. *No wonder they are content to swim around as things heat up, he's thinking. Historically, big companies have wanted it that way, but it makes us unresponsive to the rapidly evolving needs of our stakeholders. Bold Moves invite us outside the safety zone. Where would I be today if I hadn't been willing to take sizeable risks?*

His gaze drops to the stakeholder that motivated this unusual business trip—the beautiful Earth spreading out before him beneath the plane. Broad swatches of green give rise to nearby deserts and he sadly reflects on more of the dire literature that has crossed his desk in recent weeks:

Forests that stood for eons, breathing fresh air into the atmosphere have disappeared at an alarming rate in recent decades, creating the global equivalent of emphysema—a silent, invisible choking, unnoticed by most.

It's not enough that people like me, those at the top, have the freedom and the will to make Bold Moves. The intelligence and creativity of all of humanity is needed to sort out the mess we're in.

He thinks again of Ernie, and checks his watch. *He's just getting home from school*, he notes, *I'll try e-mailing him.*

What's up big guy? he writes.

----

nothing, comes the instant reply from half way around the world

thanks for my copy of jump

I didn't want you to miss out on our reading just

because I'm away, types Ernest.

----

not the same without you, replies Ernie.
you tell me what words mean

Hey, e-mail me a list of words you don't understand and I'll define them for you the best I can.

----

ok going now gramps:)

:) To you too!

Just moments later the e-mail program signals the arrival of another message from Ernie; a simple list of the words from *Jump* that he doesn't understand.

favorable
extensive :)

Ernest is both impressed and amused as he quickly searches the dictionary in his word processing program. Copying and pasting, he sends Ernie the definitions, thinking to himself, *Maybe I should point out that Ernie could check his own dictionary. I don't want him getting addicted to easy answers. Then again, my current connection with him will pass soon enough. I'll give this the personal touch for now.* His plane levels out at cruising altitude and Ernest picks up the little book, once again, settling in for a good, long read.

"Hey there!" cried Uncle Faddiest when he saw Jump's head break the water at 6:00 am sharp. "Very good, a most favorable start! You have just taken some big steps toward being in the Bold Moves business."

"What steps are those?" said Jump.

"Well, here you are, which says to me that you've chosen to be open," said Tode, "open to the idea of seeing the day as just beginning, open to exploring your dreams, open to the possibility of making the truly Bold Move of becoming a daytime frog, and open to learning to jump in the world of color!"

"But I don't even have my legs yet," said Jump.

"Whoa," said Tode. "Remember 'cup half full.' You don't need legs yet, and when you do, they will be there. Creatures always think they have to have it all together to start the Bold Moves process, but it doesn't work that way. If you already had everything you needed to make a Bold Move, you would have done it already, wouldn't you?"

"Makes sense," said Jump. "So you're saying all I need for now is to be open. Right?"

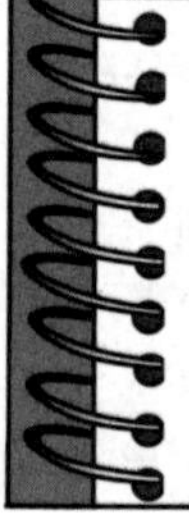

You don't need to have everything in place to begin the Bold Moves process.

"Be open, yes," said Faddiest. He smiled kindly, and then settled into a teaching mode. "You need to be open, and you need one other thing before entering Bold Moves territory. You need a map, and as it happens, I have devised a simple one to help creatures find their way in Bold Moves country. I'm going to tell you about it, and I've prepared a few things to help us get started."

He stepped aside and gestured toward several items that were arranged on the marsh bank: a Jurassic Park movie poster, a pair of stone washed hippy jeans, a Tonka™ Jeep™, and a box of ancient Jujubes™ candies.

Resting back on his strong toad legs, and seeming to gaze far off into the distance, he asked, "What do all of these things have in common?"

Jump pondered and recited; Jeans, Jeep, Jujubes. "They all begin with the letter J," he answered.

"Right you are!" said Tode. "And by the way, they are also all fads—part of my extensive fad collection. Now, if you look carefully, you'll notice that these fads have something in common with you."

Jump scrunched his face, questioning, "I'm not a fad," he said. "Am I?"

"Not yet," laughed Tode, "but if you start jumping through flaming orange hoops dressed in bright red with rhinestones, you most certainly could be a fad one day, like Elvis! But that's not the answer I was after. Look closely one more time. Here's a hint: What other word familiar to you begins with the letter J?"

"Jump! My name does."

"Correct," said Tode. "Remember when I said that your name might have more than one meaning? Well, it just so happens that your name Jump is the very name I've given to my Bold Moves map. You see my map is a set of ideas that lead in a new direction.

The ideas chart four different landscapes we must navigate as we move toward making Bold Moves. By sheer coincidence, each landscape corresponds to one of the letters of your name, J-U-M-P."

"So it's not just the name of my job?" said Jump.

"An interesting question," said Tode. "Learning a new meaning for your name might change how you think about yourself. The meaning you now give it is something you learned from your family and the other nighttime creatures of the marsh. They see it only as the name of a job to do when you grow up. We might also say that it currently means you will do that job in a particular place, the marsh, and at a particular time, the night.

"It used to be that human creatures, too, were named after the jobs they performed. Names like Carpenter, Mason, and Baker were passed down from father to son, along with the craft or trade of the same name. Many years ago, young humans began exploring the world outside their family names, so that now there are doctors named Carpenter, and lawyers named Mason."

"Those young humans must have been very bold."

"Bold, yes," said Tode, "and like many creatures today, they lived in a world of 'barely' movers. A barely moving carpenter might pound nails just the way his father and his grandfather did, but it takes a truly bold carpenter to put down his hammer and become something else, like a teacher, a fire fighter, or a diplomat. Barely Moves result from a belief that your only choice is to live from an attitude of head-down-plow-through. The attitude of Bold Moves is more like 'boldly-go-where-none-have-gone-before.'"

"Like me, a nighttime Fogg frog, going into the sunny daytime, right?" said Jump.

"Yes," said Tode. "For everyone the challenge of boldness is different because the challenge of each individual future is unique. I was using a change in occupation, before, only as an example."

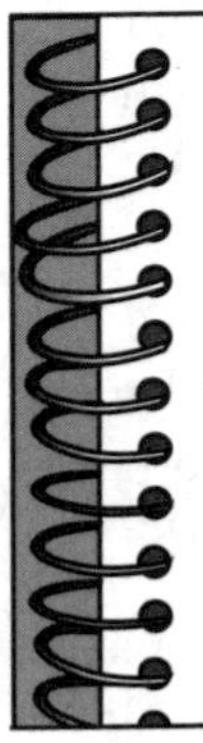

Which of your moves have others scripted for you?

Which moves have been conscious decisions derived from your own sense of passion and purpose?

"Do you think I'm bold enough to jump through flaming orange hoops?" asked Jump.

"You can only know the answer to that question if you accept the challenge of your future by asking yourself, "How outrageous can my Bold Move be? Dare I conceive it? Am I willing to be it?

"I suspect that by the time you find flaming hoops in your future, you'll be plenty bold enough to jump through them. That's the easy part. Getting to that very different place and time is the challenge.

It's worth a try, though, because in today's world, if you want to succeed in creating a big impact, hard work and black-and-white answers are not what's needed. Only those who are willing to make Bold Moves in smart and purposeful ways can make the big contributions in their professional and personal lives. Makers of Bold Moves come up with answers in all the colors of the rainbow. As we will see, they also create lives that have a surprising sense of ease about them."

"That sounds great," said Jump, "and a little scary."

"Of course," said Tode, "if the idea didn't stretch you quite a bit, it wouldn't require you to be bold, would it?"

"But maybe I'm not bold," said Jump.

"That is for you to determine over time," said Tode. "However, I can think of eight moves you've already made that show boldness. One, you dared to listen to your dreams. Two, you shared them with Plop and Croak. Three, even when your siblings tried to diminish your dreams, you believed in them enough to share them with your mom and dad. Four, you woke up yesterday while it was still daytime. Five, you came to find me. Six, you turned your night upside-down last night, sleeping when you normally would be jumping. Seven, you opened to seeing the day as just beginning by getting up early for the first time in your life. Eight, you opened to the possibility of making a truly Bold Move and becoming a daytime frog by honoring our appointment this morning. Do you know of any other nighttime frogs who've done any of those things?"

"No," Jump replied, "I really was not giving myself credit."

"Most frogs allow their dreams to fade into the night," said Faddiest. "But you didn't, and it led you to the opportunity to learn about making Bold Moves."

There was a definite sparkle of excitement in Jump's eyes as he accepted the compliment, but Tode could tell the tadpole was approaching overload. *So many new ideas*, he thought, *and it's the middle of his normal sleep time*.

"Our session is about over for today," he said. "Tomorrow we will get back to our Bold Moves map, and look more closely at the landscape of J, the first letter of your name.

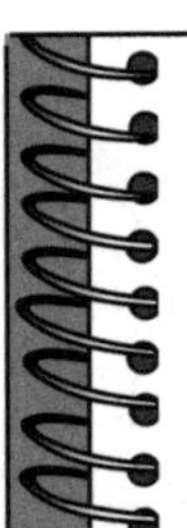

Notice and record the steps you have already taken toward your Bold Move.

NINE

On Tour with Jackson McPlayer, Interstate 10 near LaSalle, Illinois

Pulling into the Flying J™ truck stop, Jackson's tour caravan awes truckers, bikers and tourists alike. In the lead, its trailer graphically shrink-wrapped in fiery rings of orange, red and purple, is a custom Peterbilt™ 379X cab, chosen for its 'pulse pounding polished aluminum on chrome' and prompted by ad copy asserting it to be 'a reflection of the independent soul and entrepreneurial spirit of today's owner.' Home to six Harleys, the semi also carries two tons of AV equipment, ramps, hoops, chemicals, costumes and other show gear. Following closely comes McPlayer himself in his matching custom Winnebago™ Vectra. Loving the open road, he insists on being his own driver.

Next in the entourage is a flatbed rig, piggybacking two white draft horses in an oversized equestrian trailer, and a magnificent 1911 Ahrens-Fox™ Steam Engine. Bringing both nostalgia and safety to Jackson's fiery performance, the horse drawn fire-fighting antique is retrofitted with the latest fire extinguishing chemicals and computerized applicators. Bringing up the rear, a five-man roadie crew rides in a gaseous hydrogen fueled Hummer®.

Taken all together, the convoy looks like a high tech circus––not far from the truth. Technically on the leading edge, and ecologically friendly, the assemblage far outpaces competitors in both style and brand recognition.

But dare devil jumping is only one of Jackson's professional endeavors. Doing business under a name that is less 'show-biz', he has developed a high-end coaching practice working with business and government leaders in the making of Bold Moves. All of Jackson's sessions are delivered by phone, cell-phone actually, from the road. In fact, a call will come any minute from a private jet cruising somewhere over the Pacific Ocean.

"This is Putnam," he says checking caller ID. "How's the weather over Fiji, Ernest?"

"Smooth enough for flying," says Cottingham, "but the frog hunt isn't going very well."

"No jumpers yet, eh?" says Joe.

"Nope, it seems like the frogs in the company pot want to keep on swimming no matter what the water temperature is. I'd like to know what they're telling themselves when they look in the mirror."

"Where are you in the book?" asks Putnam.

"Just getting started really. Old Tode just introduced the acronym J-U-M-P, but I've got plenty of time to read between here and my layover at home."

They converse for nearly an hour, discussing the sizeable challenge Ernest has before him and Joe completes the call saying, "I think you'll be quite intrigued by the meaning of J. When you do finally find your jumping frog, it will be your job to teach the lessons of J, U, M and P, so keep your head up on this."

"Sure thing," says Cottingham. "Ernie is a help there. He keeps me at attention on the book. It's like he already knows this stuff, even though he doesn't understand half of the words."

"It's the kid thing," says Joe. "Possibility comes natural to them until it gets trained out. Maybe Ernie will escape that fate."

"He will if I have anything to say about it," says Ernest, ending the call.

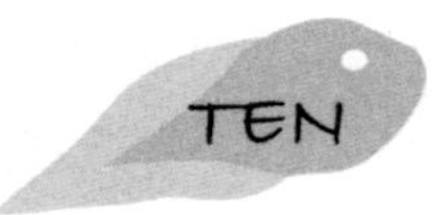

TEN

Global Thrills, Inc. Corporate Jet, Somewhere Over the Pacific

I'll be glad for the break at home, Ernest is thinking, *before my flight out to Kalamazoo tomorrow. If Evelyn Dodd is everything I think she is, she's looking a lot like my frog of last resort.* He thumbs open the Jump book and reads on.

The sun was only a promise of light at the eastern horizon when Jump lifted his head near the water's edge, but Faddiest was there to greet him in his warm and dignified manner.

"Good morning," he said. "Welcome to the landscape of J."

While he talked, he was laying out a bright red jump rope with wooden handles on the ends. Forming it on the ground, he made a giant letter J.

"This is the first of four landscapes we will explore on your way to making Bold Moves," he said, quite formally. "The landscape of J. which stands for 'Justify Nothing.'"

Justify Nothing, thought Jump. "What does it mean?" he asked.

Taking a step back to examine his work, Tode adjusted the bottom curve of the J and glanced sideways to check for any effect his words might be having on Jump. "Well," he said, "let's look at the word 'justify.' According to my dictionary, it means, 'To prove or show to be just, or correct, according to the rules of law, logic, or commonly accepted societal agreements.'"

It must be said here, that along with his vivid imagination, Jump also possessed a keen sense of right and wrong, and a blossoming aptitude for reasoning. So, although he didn't entirely understand why, the words "Justify Nothing," poked uncomfortably at the way he saw the world. A wave of caution washed over him.

Without thinking, he said, "And you're saying 'Justify Nothing?'"

At the same moment, an urgent warning voice sounded inside Jump's head. *Watch out!* it said. *The old toad might be a little crazy! Be careful! He's telling you that your thoughts and actions don't have to make logical good sense. He's saying you don't have to be an honorable person.* The warning gained in strength and volume until Jump found he had ducked down into deep gray marsh water to shut it out.

Watching the ripple from the sudden departure, Faddiest was thinking, it is always frightening at first, opening the mind in new ways. If he's really ready, he'll be back.

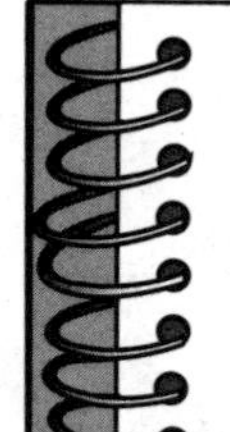

Don't let fear of new thoughts and ideas keep you from exploring new possibilities.

Hidden in shadows a short way off, Jump felt the voice of fear settling down a bit until it spit out a final, almost listless, *Justify Nothing. What a nutty idea!* Moments later, Jump's composure returned and his curiosity lifted him back up toward the marsh bank.

Faddiest spoke to him patiently. "What did it say?" he asked.

"What did who say?" said Jump.

"The Inner Critter voice in your mind," said Tode.

Reluctant to tell Uncle Tode about all the bad things the voice had said about him, Jump asked, "How did you know I heard an Inner Critter?"

"It's my job to know when the voices of doubt and fear are present in the coaching conversation," said Tode. "Do you remember when we talked about them before?"

"Yes," said Jump. "You said if I decided to learn about making Bold Moves, I would come to hear the voices of doubt and fear in my ear, and I would hear them as different from the other voice, The Whisperer."

"The Whisperer being the 'yes' voice of possibility," said Tode, emphasizing the importance of the distinction. "That's right. The voices you were hearing just now—the ones that had you diving for cover—were definitely not The Whisperer, they were Inner Critters."

"I don't like them," said Jump. "They make me feel a little sick."

"Maybe that's good," said Tode. "Perhaps the sick feeling is your body's way of bringing your attention to those voices and showing you how troublesome they truly are."

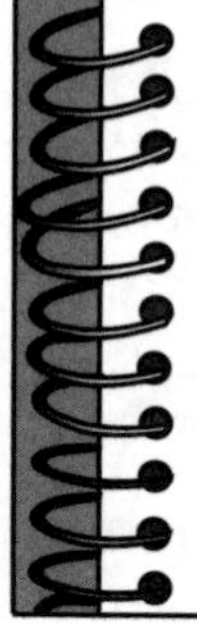

Inner Critters are negative mind chatter. The discomfort they bring can be a wake up call pointing to unrecognized fears.

"They said you might be crazy," admitted Jump, reluctantly.

"That is not at all surprising," said Tode. "Inner Critters love to criticize anyone who offers new possibilities."

"Will The Whisperer talk to me too?" asked Jump.

"It already has," said Tode. "It spoke in your dreams about the daytime world of bright colors. Yesterday, I think I heard it right along with your own frog voice when you said that big, excited. 'Yes' in answer to my question about whether you could stay up until morning. The Whisperer also helped you wake up at dawn today when you worried you might not be able to."

Jump nodded, remembering the powerful voice that spoke in his dream, saying the words, *I simply will wake up.*

"It sure didn't seem like a whisper," said Jump.

"That's because you are still so young," said Tode. "Very young creatures of all sorts can hear The Whisperer loud and clear. Over time the 'yes' voice becomes lost in thousands of messages from the outside world. Most of my very important adult coaching clients can barely hear it at all when they first come to me."

Can you tell who has the microphone in your head at any given time?

The Whisperer?

The Inner Critters?

"Oh yes," said Tode. "For the most part, I'd say Inner Critters have taken up command stations in the minds of adults creatures, and are exerting frighteningly high levels of control over their thoughts and actions. That is why the first of the Bold Moves landscapes clients must explore is Justify Nothing."

"I don't quite get it," said Jump.

"Well," said Tode, "I haven't yet told you the whole story: and there's a reason for that. You see, whenever I first say the words 'Justify Nothing,' I always watch for the reaction I get. As often as not, my words wake up Inner Critters, offering a rich opportunity for identifying them, just as it did for you. The next step is for me to reveal the full name for the J landscape. It is Justify Nothing—Inside Yourself."

"That's where my Inner Critters are," Jump said, "inside myself."

"Yes," said Tode, "but they become very uncomfortable when you enter the landscape of Justify Nothing—Inside Yourself. Your Inner Critters hope to keep you in the place of 'justify everything.'"

"Why?"

"Because when you are caught up in the world of 'justify everything,' distracted by doubt and fear, you don't have the time or energy to make Bold Moves. You are focused on the world outside of yourself, worried about what others will think or say. This is rich territory for Inner Critters who will say just about anything to keep you looking to the outside for approval.

"When you enter the landscape of Justify Nothing—Inside Yourself and move toward making a Bold Move, your Inner Critters get very upset because your attention becomes focused inside where you can shine the spotlight on Inner Critters and expose them for what they are, mere shadows of fear and doubt."

Fascinated, Jump asked, "Does anyone live in the landscape of Justify Nothing—Inside Yourself?"

"The Whisperer does," said Tode. "The Whisperer is the grounds keeper for the landscape of Justify Nothing—Inside Yourself. It is the voice that plants the seeds of Bold Moves, and gives you the patience and courage to tend and foster them as they develop."

Cottingham closes the book and summarizes his understanding of the J in J-U-M-P as his plane lands in Burbank.

Justify Nothing

- Get inside yourself
- Notice where you're holding yourself small
- Find the courage and patience to make a Bold Move
- The Bold Moves process naturally evokes Inner Critters
- The goal is to learn to identify and eventually manage your Critter voices.

ELEVEN

Executive Lounge, Private Jet Terminal, Burbank, CA

After a good night's sleep in his own bed, Ernest is waiting to board his jet and thinking about his frog hunt. *With the J of Jump in mind, I can see how my employees might judge themselves small when they look to the outside world around them. Then, of course—because they're expecting to—they see further evidence for their self-judgments. In order to play it safe, then, they think and act small, entering an endless loop of limiting beliefs and actions that get smaller and smaller. This is the circle of the frog swimming in the pot. But what can I do about it? Surely there are those who long to hold themselves as bigger—as bolder? How can I help? He returns to his book, seeking answers.*

> Jump said, "Boy, those Inner Critters are really tricky. They made me worry that you were telling me to do things I didn't feel good about."
>
> "Hmmm," said Tode, "that is a timely report, because, you see, it is very important that you understand I'm not the least bit interested in telling you what you need to <u>do</u> in order to make Bold Moves. I'm interested, only, in how you might choose to <u>be</u>."
>
> Jump found himself pulled ahead once more, into a place he'd never been, and asked, "How I might

choose to be?"

"Yes. 'Being' is the very best way to approach the landscape of Justify Nothing where your seeds of Bold Moves await you."

Jump's head was nodding as he tried to grasp Tode's meaning, but Faddiest saw sure signs of overload in the way the tadpole's eyes had trouble staying in focus. "Let's have a break," he said. "I suggest you take the rest of the morning and just 'be' by yourself. Can you do that?"

You might be broken down
because no one is telling you
to take a break.

Take the morning off
just to "be" you,
not to "do" anything.

Can I just 'be' by myself? Another first time question. It hit Jump's brain like a ping-pong ball and forced out another "Yes."

Immediately, his Inner Critters took hold of his tongue and spat out, "But I'm supposed to work hard at learning my job of waking up the creatures of the marsh! And besides, everything's so different in the daylight, I'm nearly blinded by it."

Faddiest watched carefully to see if Jump noticed that he had let his Inner Critter take charge and boomerang him, once again, from 'yes' to 'I don't think so.' The answer came in the form of a knowing blush that filled Jump's green cheeks, spreading until it covered his head nearly to his tail.

"I'll try," he said without prompting, "I'll try to 'be' by myself."

"Watch those Critters," said Uncle Tode with a wink. "As you said, they are pretty tricky."

Jump accepted his assignment in earnest. '*Be*', he thought to himself, *I've got to 'be' by myself.* He didn't have the slightest clue what that really meant. His frames of reference until just two days before had been dedication to work and trying hard to please his parents, so it was natural that he would go about 'being' in a dedicated and serious manner. He shook his tail wildly until he was speeding through the water of the marsh. His wake washed through a school of minnows, scattering them every which way.

"Is this right?" he asked as they scrambled to regroup. "Am I 'being'?"

"Being disruptive!" answered an angry chorus of tiny voices. "And messing us up."

"I didn't mean to . . ." said Jump. "I was practicing 'being' and I just didn't . . ," but his apology was drowned out by a rush of bubbles as the tiny fish collected themselves and swam off in perfect formation.

A creepy feeling came over Jump. His heart pounded and he felt awkward and a little guilty as a voice inside him said, *You really blew that one! How Rude!*

I'll try again, he thought, *and try and try until I*

am 'being' for sure. Swimming off to the corner of the marsh that had been his family's home for eons, he forgot that it was day. When he arrived, everyone was sleeping.

"I'm learning to 'be'," he called, "and I need your help."

Croak was the first to hear him. Turning away from the racket Jump was making, he soon found he couldn't go back to sleep. Through one tired eye, he watched his brother perform acrobatics and try out new strokes thinking, *what's gotten into him?*

Jump whirled to a stop right over Croak's head and said, "Am I being?"

"Being?" asked Croak, annoyed. Remembering how Skita had told him to 'be' a good tadpole, he answered, "Being bad, if you ask me. And you'll never be good if you keep waking everyone up." Pulling a fat blade of marsh grass over him, he rolled over and mumbled, "You're supposed to practice at night when everyone is awake."

Once again, Jump felt the need to explain, "Uncle Tode says 'being' is important if you want to make Bold . . ," but he got no more response from Croak.

Bad, bad, said his Critters, *Croak is right, you are being very bad, splashing around and waking creatures up.*

You shouldn't have made so much noise, Jump said to himself, not realizing that his words came from his Inner Critters or that he was caught in a rash of Brash Moves.

He swam on, recovering a little, until he neared

the marsh bank where Dermand slept. His father rose up in a daze wondering who was stirring in the middle of the day. There was Jump diving through blinding sparkles on the water's surface.

"Hi Dad," he called. "Is this what you call 'being'?"

"I'd call it being far too bright eyed for this time of day," Dermand said, squinting against the glare of the sun. "Go back to sleep or you'll be too tired for jumping tonight."

"But I'm trying to 'be'!" Jump explained.

"Keep your trying for the work at hand," yawned Dermand drifting off again.

Jump was overcome by disappointment. With the weight of his father's disapproval on their side, his Inner Critters began a litany of should's, shouldn't's, and shame-on-you's, culminating in; *You should just go to sleep like everyone else and forget about learning to 'be'.*

But the vision of the orange hoop flamed up in Jump's mind reminding him of his desire to make Bold Moves. *Those hoops are in your future somewhere*, said his strong clear Whisperer voice. *Your next step toward them is to learn how to 'be' by yourself.*

Leaving his family in slumber, Jump swam in wider circles to where the daytime creatures of the marsh were going about their morning chores. Swishing by a water beetle, he asked, "Is this how to 'be'?" He thought surely a daytime creature would know about 'being'.

In a disgusted tone the lanky beetle said, "You

are not a bee. You are a tadpole, and not a very bright one at that it seems!"

Not very bright at all, said Jump's Inner Critters. *Being! How ridiculous.*

Hearing the exchange, an old coot in a nearby tree rustled his few motley feathers and cautioned, "Be safe there, young tadpole!"

Jump's Critters echoed, *Be safe or you'll be sorry! There's safety in numbers and you are all alone, Jump. Safety is as safety does, and what you are doing is risky business!*

Well meaning people in your close circle of family and friends can impose inordinate pressure to keep you from "being" yourself.

They unwittingly serve as allies to your Inner Critters.

Even messages from strangers (and media) can add weight to the self-judgments voiced by your Inner Critters.

The long shadows of nearby elms inched their way homeward, and paused beneath the trees themselves. Mid-day found Jump floating listlessly in the deepest hole of the marsh. Tiny bubbles escaped his gills in the steady breaths of slumber. Exhausted and dispirited, he had finally nodded off. In his dream, an Inner Critter was saying to Uncle Faddiest, *"No, I can't 'be' by myself. I don't know how, and nobody else seems to know either. And now I'm so tired I don't care if I ever learn to 'be'."*

A sand hill crane was sleeping too, atop a single leg with the foot buried in mud directly under the exhausted tadpole. Awakened by the hot sun on his back, the great bird lifted into flight, tumbling Jump into a thick swirl of silt and rotting plant matter. The tadpole's eyes popped open. A final bubble escaped his gills in a gasp and he darted upward.

Breaking the surface, he was overwhelmed by brilliant color all around him; ten shades of greens from lime to olive, blues from aqua to royal. Jump was so amazed, he nearly forgot to be concerned that noontime had come, and maybe even gone. *While I was sleeping,* he thought finally, recalling his appointment with Faddiest. *I must have slept for hours.*

That was enough to start his Critters up again: *You should still be sleeping. Go back to bed; it's the middle of the day! You didn't learn how to be, and you never will.*

From the marsh bank, Faddiest cast his gaze steadily on Jump, who rambled on about how he got so tired he fell asleep. "And no, I can't 'be' by myself," he said in a Critter voice just as he had in his dream, and added, "Why is 'being' important anyway? How will it help me find the raspberry red Star Dude suit?"

"It is entirely possible to wear oneself out 'being'," Faddiest said, interjecting, "but it's a wearing out that leaves you feeling good, and it seems to me you're feeling pretty bad right now. Tell me what happened. Didn't you like seeing the colors of the day? Smelling the scents of the sun warmed shores?"

"What colors?" asked Jump, "All I saw was muddy brown when I woke up on the bottom of the marsh! And before I fell asleep, I only smelled a muskrat who swam away yelling 'to be, or not to be,' when I asked him if I was 'being' correctly."

"How do you 'be', anyway?' he continued. "And why should I do it?" The questions hung there while more stories rolled off his long amphibian tongue, complicated tales of a frustrating morning. Once they were told, Jump grew sad. "I tried and tried to 'be' by myself," he said, "but no matter what I did, I couldn't get it right. Where did I go wrong, Uncle Faddiest?"

"Listen carefully, son," said Faddiest. "What I'm about to say is very important. You see, the answer is simple on the surface, but truly understanding it isn't easy."

Jump was all ears as Tode paused to give his point added emphasis. "'Being' isn't about doing it right or doing it wrong. 'Being' is about that different state of mind that we move into by experiencing the world from the inside out instead of from the outside in. One way we can tell if we're truly 'being' or not, is by noticing whether or not we feel the need to 'justify everything' we do. Think about your morning. You spent it trying to explain what you were doing—like to the minnows, to Croak and Dermand, and to the rude beetle."

Jump nodded his head in recognition. "I spent the whole morning asking others if I was doing 'being' right."

"So you did," said Tode, "and each of them answered your questions in their own way. From what you've told me, none were very encouraging. Think of the old coot that told you to 'be' safe. I happen to know he scared himself silly one spring flying upside down in a windy migration. He took a nosedive, landed on that elm limb, and has been there ever since, afraid to take off again. His feathers are falling out because he hasn't flapped his wings in years!"

"Now I get it," said Jump. "I spent the morning 'justifying' the fact that I was trying to 'be.' I felt I needed to 'justify everything.' It made me feel bad when others didn't understand."

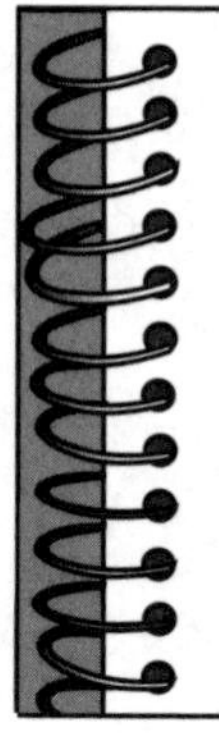

Doing for "doing's" sake is reactive, on the order of a Brash Move.

Doing for "doing's" sake depletes energy and precludes a sense of fulfillment.

"Something happened when you started feeling bad," said Tode. "Do you know what I'm talking about?"

"Well, I just felt worse and worse. I felt bad, and wrong, and even selfish."

"What was it that made you feel all of those things?"

"It's like I kept telling myself I shouldn't be doing what I was doing."

"Only one part of you was saying those things," said Tode. "Do you know what part that was?"

Jump thought carefully through what had happened that morning. He could almost hear one particular message ringing out in his head: *You should just go to sleep like everyone else and forget about learning to 'be'.*

"It was my Inner Critters talking," he said finally.

"Those Inner Critters really got feisty," said Tode.

"How do you tell it's the Critters talking, right when it's happening?" asked Jump.

"Their messages are always filled with doubt and fear," said Tode, "remember?

"Though they come from inside you, Critters are stimulated by your reactions to the messages of the world outside of you.

"We'll answer more of your questions when we meet tomorrow," said Tode. "Let's say about ten thirty in the morning. You can take some time for yourself until then."

Jump felt relieved. His sleep pattern was mixed up and part of him longed for his cozy waterbed. He was eager, though, for more of Uncle's new ideas. "I'll be here," he said and ducked down into the wet, blue marsh.

Inner Critter messages are messages of doubt and fear.

As the water gets hotter and hotter, Inner Critter messages keep the swimming frog's focus on the limited reality of the inside walls of the pot

There, he sees his doubts and fears continually mirrored back at him.

For the rest of the afternoon, Faddiest prepared his back-up plan for the lesson on 'being.' *I'll stimulate all five of his senses*, he was thinking. *Hmm, let's see, I have the perfect fad to wake up his ears—Boy Bands.* Playing an N Sync™ cut on his iPod™, he gave it a little of the twist. Gobstoppers® and reasonably fresh Pop Tarts® were chosen for taste. For touch, he found Kooshballs™ and Silly Putty™. A psychedelic poster would work for the eyes, but he couldn't decide on a proper scent for Jump's nasal sensors. *I'll think of something,* he said to himself before retiring for the evening.

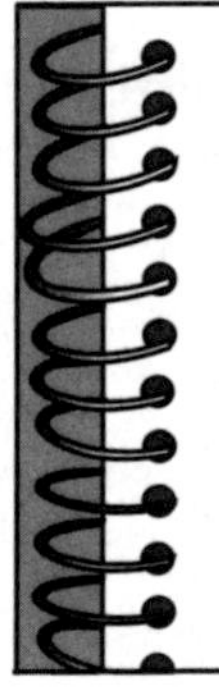

Awaken all of your senses and explore new points of view.

See, hear, taste, touch and smell fresh possibilities.

Dawn came again, and when Faddiest saw Jump, the difference in the young one's demeanor was striking. Floating tummy up on a lily pad with the back of his head cradled in moss, the tadpole gazed contentedly into the mid-morning sky. Bumping gently to shore, his makeshift raft flipped over, depositing him on the marsh bank with a huge smile on his face.

"What a morning," he said.

Faddiest instantly knew he wouldn't need all the faddish things he'd sorted out for the session on how to 'be.' *No, he's there already,* he thought. *It's time to just listen.*

Unable to contain his excitement, Jump effused a state of pure 'being,' "Did you know that the clouds turn bright red when the sun comes up? And if you poke into a hollow log, a snail will squirt you with slime? I broke a cattail open and I sneezed and sneezed 'til I couldn't help laughing at myself."

On and on he went, exquisitely detailing the sights, sounds, smells and feel of his marshland world. "A hummingbird lifted straight up from its perch and hovered in the air with wings so fast I could only see a blur, but it made such a busy sound! And did you know that spicebush smells ever so sweet? I saw one making blossoms out of tiny golden halos. Oh, and caterpillars! They come in every color of the rainbow, with stripes and dots!"

"Everything seems so alive," he said, finally, "and so magical! Like I've been in a dream wide-awake. What's happened to me Uncle Faddiest?"

"That's 'being'," Tode said at last. "You've done it Jump; you've learned how to 'be'." Letting the notion sink in a moment, he asked, "Tell me how it all began."

"It just seemed to happen when I woke up this morning before dawn," Jump answered. "First I heard the quiet of the pond as the night creatures stopped their croaking and plopping. Then I heard the call of a bird, and it just went on from there, like I was in a dream. 'Being' and dreaming are a lot alike, aren't they? Except you don't exactly wake up from 'being'."

"They are similar," said Faddiest, "and no you don't wake up from 'being', exactly, but you do make a similar kind of change in your state of mind when you go from 'doing' to 'being.' Human creatures call it 'taking time to smell the roses,' and it's one of the hardest things for them to do in their busy lives. Humans, and most frogs too, miss a lot. As you have seen, there are many things in addition to roses, to smell--and see."

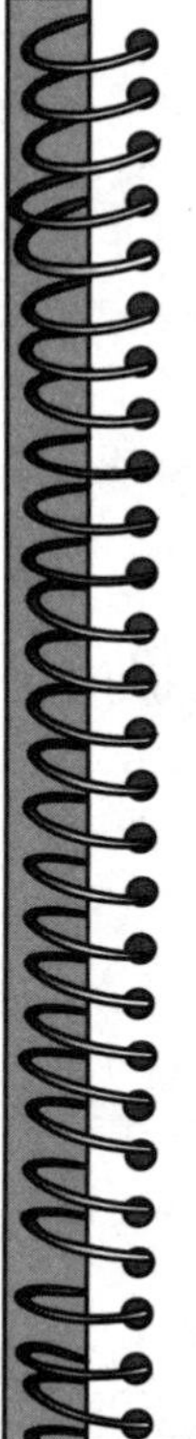

Doing for "being's" sake is proactive. It is energizing and leads to a sense of fulfillment.

The frog in the pot turns his gaze upward away from the limiting walls of the pot.

There, he glimpses unexplored terrain that offers previously unseen possibilities.

Note: I had a little trouble reading this part on 'being.' It was hard for me to slow down enough to 'smell the roses.'

"Most creatures never examine a spicebush that's budding—even those who have spicebushes right in their gardens. They can't slow down enough. 'Being' is about the relaxed state of mood you're in when you allow yourself the pleasure of noticing the small treasures and pleasures in life, when you open to a much more expansive sense of reality."

"But it feels so good, why don't creatures want to notice?" asked Jump.

"They're too busy justifying why they should

stay focused on other things," said Tode.

"'Being' begins by choosing to look at the world from the inside out. That's why it's easier to do when you're just waking up after spending hours deep inside yourself. You are already relaxed—unless, of course, like many human creatures, you have an alarm clock freaking you out first thing every morning."

The world constantly prompts you to search externally for ideas and inspiration.

Bold Move seeds are internal not external.

The frog in the pot first closes his eyes and dreams of a different world.

This gives him the presence of mind to think of looking in a new direction--up.

In his short life, Jump had never seen a human, but Tode had a way of describing them. "Is there any way for human creatures to stay relaxed long enough to smell the spicebush?" asked Jump.

"Of course. They can start by doing simple things. Walk past the TV set and the computer without turning them on. Go outside. Ignore the billboard across the street. Tune out the radio blaring from a neighbor's car. Don't pick up the newspaper or the mail until later in the day. Be very careful to maintain an inward focus."

"Then open your inner eyes to the natural world. Look for points of curiosity and follow them. Move in close to a bird's nest. Check for tiny creatures there. Track the wind in the leaves that blow down the street. Follow your own sense of wonder."

At the beginning of the Bold Move process, there is no gift box, fully wrapped

--only hints and clues to be explored.

Consider everything, no editing, and no "justifying everything."

"Ah," said Jump, still feeling very relaxed and as Faddiest would say, 'open'. "So let me get this straight. You're saying that when I saw the sunrise, and when I poked my finger in the log, and when I broke open the cattail—when I was 'being'—I was seeing the world from the inside out?"

Tode answered with questions of his own, "Did anyone tell you to do those things?"

"No."

"Were you the least bit worried about whether you were doing them right?"

"No. I just did 'em."

"Why?"

"I just wanted to."

"Yes," said Tode, "you were following your own inner directions—looking at the world as only you could look at it, from your inside out. You were deciding all by yourself what you wanted to explore. You were simply 'being.'"

"Wow," Jump said, "when you learn how to 'be, and start seeing the world from the inside out . . . it's beautiful!"

"And you find that it's okay to 'Justify Nothing––Inside Yourself,' said Tode, his grin nearly wrapping clear around his head. *All the fad props in the world couldn't teach the lesson better,* he was thinking. *Jump has experienced 'being'. He has seen the world through his very own eyes, without any parent voices in his head, or any old coots or timid minnows. There were no Inner Critters taunting him to 'justify everything.' What's more, he sees that he has seen it that way, and he likes what he's seen. There is much to work with here . . . much to work with.*

"There are a lot of lessons to remember in the landscape of Justify Nothing," said Jump. "There's being open; seeing the world as 'cup half full' instead of 'cup half empty' (or seeing the day as always beginning instead of always ending;) and there's viewing the world from the inside-out instead of from the outside-in. There's also learning to hear your Inner Critter voices and The Whisperer. Whew!"

This little guy is as bright as a hand painted tie, thought Tode, scratching his warts for inspiration, *but I don't want to overwhelm him. How can I make this easier to understand?* Gazing off a bit, he spied a stately elm tree. On the ground beneath it was a smattering of seeds just ripe for planting. Hopping gingerly to pick one up, he returned saying, "You came to me with a dream of jumping through the flaming orange hoop. In the days since, we have learned that there is a Bold Move you must make if you are to find the flaming hoop—the Bold Move of becoming a daytime frog."

Giving the elm seed to Jump, he continued, "Let's pretend your Bold Move is this elm seed. If we want it to grow, we must prepare the soil for it. First, you'll need to hollow out a hole someplace here on the marsh bank."

Jump knew right where to plant his seed: inside the landscape of Justify Nothing—Inside Yourself, in the curved part of the big jump rope J.

"Clever," said Tode as Jump began to dig, "a perfect place for it!"

Digging in dirt was a significant effort for a tadpole. Uncle Faddiest helped by making a small indentation and filling it with water. Jump slid into the tiny puddle that formed and found that by using his tail and his mouth, he could do the digging required in time to return to the marsh water for a proper breath through his gills. The ground was soft and damp, so the hole came quickly.

When it was deep enough for planting, Tode said, "Now dive down to the bottom of the pond and wrap your tongue around some rich black mud to put in that hole."

Soon the hole was lined with nutritious mud, and Jump used his tail to push the elm seed inside. Filling the hole to cover the seed, they heard a little 'blurp' made by an air bubble rising through the mud to the surface. "Hey, the seed is talking!" Jump said, poking fun.

In his wisdom, Tode knew that every breath and sigh in the world around him could be read for deeper meaning. "Perhaps it's The Whisperer giving us a high five," he said. "As you prepare yourself for growing your Bold Move, you will begin to hear The Whisperer tending the fertile soil inside of you."

"There's fertile soil inside me to grow my Bold Move seed?" Jump asked.

"Your fertile soil is a state of mind you begin to develop by learning all of the lessons in the landscape of Justify Nothing—Inside Yourself," said Tode. "I call that state of mind your Optimal Operating State–—your personal state of calm and composure that will sustain you as you learn to make Bold Moves."

"My Optimal Operating State," said Jump repeating words that felt too big for him.

"Yes," said Tode. "It will make more sense to you as we venture into the landscape of the U of J-U-M-P. You see in the J of J-U-M-P you develop your Optimal Operating State. You hollow out the ground making space for new thoughts and ideas; you learn about Inner Critters and The Whisperer, and you plant the seed of a Bold Move like your possibility of becoming a daytime frog. As you continue into the U of J-U-M-P, you will learn to support and sustain your Optimal Operating State. You will see more of who you are and what you bring to making your Bold Move.

"First, though, it would be good to let the lessons of J sink in a bit. The J landscape is a place where you can't cheat. If you do, you only cheat yourself. You might be able to fool me and make me think you're not justifying, but you can't fool yourself. If you don't get the lessons of J clear and straight, it's like you are polluted when you get to the U of J-U-M-P, and then the lessons you learn there are not clear; they're murky and cloudy.

"Let's give you a few days to think about Justify Nothing—Inside Yourself and meet again on Thursday."

"I'll be here," said Jump without hesitation.

They stayed, then, for a few more minutes, silently celebrating the planted seed and the coaching bond that was forming between them. Tode straddled a stump with one leg stretched nearly to the ground. Jump swayed gently in the cool marsh water of the springtime afternoon. They were in a state of 'being' together. It was a moment to savor.

Ernest makes one last series of notes in the Reader's Log.

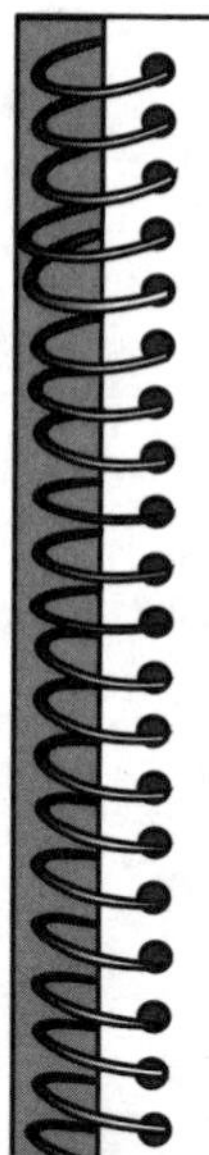

The J of J-U-M-P gets you ready to define the foundation of who you are.

J makes you aware of your Optimal Operating State as you learn all of the lessons of

Justify Nothing--Inside Yourself.

LESSONS of Justify Nothing--Inside Yourself:

• Be open to new possibilities.

• See the world as "cup half full" instead of "cup half empty."

• View the world from the inside out instead of from the outside in.

More lessons of Justify Nothing--Inside Yourself:

• Identify your Inner Critters

• Listen carefully for The Whisperer.

• Notice who has the microphone in your head

• Give yourself the space to develop your Optimal Operating State.

• Go to nature; get away from what you know in your everyday life.

• Wake up to a world that offers permission and skills for turning attention inward without being consumed by negative self-talk, nor overly influenced by the judgments of others.

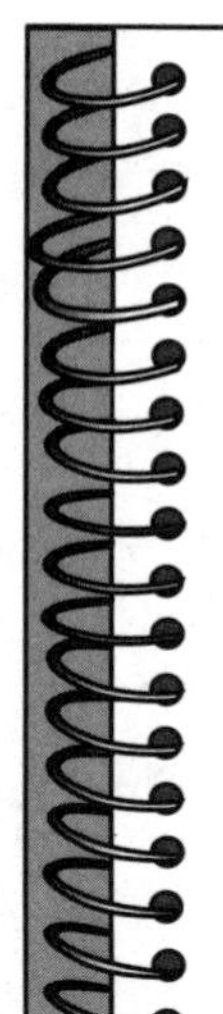

The J of J-U-M-P has you develop your Optimal Operating State.

The U has you learn to support and sustain it.

Justify Nothing--
Inside Yourself

Ernest's attention is drawn away from his notes by a voice on the executive lounge paging system. It says, and then repeats, "Mr. Cottingham, your plane is ready for boarding on the south tarmac."

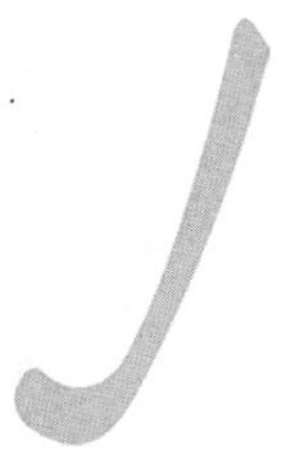

TWELVE

Global Thrills Arena, Kalamazoo, Michigan

Evelyn Dodd might have saved her excitement about the weekend that was now upon her. No sooner does Jackson U. McPlayer pull his tour caravan onto the lot than her enthusiasm hits a wall. She has known he intends to debut a new ending to his act today, but it isn't until this very moment, ten o'clock Saturday morning—just hours before the matinee—that she realizes the extent of the change, and the compromising position it potentially poses for her.

You see, Jackson McPlayer is not really a buffed out Harley guy. Inside a carefully crafted public image, he is a quiet, thoughtful soul who, with Evelyn's help, and the aide of numerous technological devices, has been able to project the image of a daredevil Harley rider. Now, Jackson, or Joe Putnam, as his coaching clients know him, wants his fans to know the truth of his identity.

"It's unacceptable," Evelyn says, speaking into the two-way communication device Jackson had devised as part of his disguise. "You simply can't do it."

No one has seen the stunt because, as usual, Jackson's rehearsals are private. Long years of working with a coach of his own have made him aware that he needs full concentration and solitude to work out his moves. A natural aptitude for working with computerized technology provides him a method to perfect his craft in solitude. Instead of taking the bike through real action, he uses simulations.

At show time, the rider goes through his moves, and when the stunts are done and the first layer of Jackson's reflective visor recesses into the helmet, it reveals a daredevil face. It's a move that sends his fans into ecstasy, and that's what they know of him—until today.

Today, after completing the jump of a lifetime, Jackson will reveal for the first time, the closely held secret that drives his success. This afternoon, after he smiles his finale smile in a slow 360 turn around the perimeter of the arena, he'll pull to the center, cameras close up on his helmet, and the face in the visor will magically dissolve, showing itself for the hologram it truly is.

This day, Jackson's public image will change forever and his true identity and genius will be displayed.

"We have already discussed this," he says to Evelyn. "You've had the technical plans for a month."

"I didn't understand," she replies. "I leave the tech stuff to my staff. You know that. Your plan wasn't clear to me. This simply can't happen."

She insists that Jackson's upcoming stunt does not fall within corporate's risk management profile. His numbers are already great and Evelyn doesn't want him rocking the boat.

"I can see how powerful your new ending could be if it's successful," she says finally, "but Global's CEO, Ernest Cottingham, is on some mysterious trip reviewing some of my top competition in the company. I can't be taking a risk right now. He doesn't know you're not what you seem. There's no way I'm going to let him get wind of it under conditions that could cost me my job."

"I won't change the show at the last minute," says Jackson, firmly but unperturbed, "but I will take full responsibility if my choice to debut the new ending leads to any negative results. You have my word on that."

THIRTEEN

Global Thrills, Inc. Corporate Jet, Over the Nevada Desert

Ernest glances at the arid land below. We're heading for a global desert, he's thinking. It's so silly. With the amount of sunshine hitting Nevada alone, we could power with solar energy the entire western United States. Then the big rivers could run free and the oceans might have a chance to heal themselves. His imagination chronicles a dozen other solutions that could be applied to the many issues plaguing the earth, until he's summoned once again by an incoming e-mail.

hi gramps. thanks for the definitions

You're welcome. Where are you in the book?

----

reading about the letter U. you? lol

Just a little behind you. Sorry I couldn't see you while I was home. It was a quick stop.

----

its ok

more words i don't understand
outrageous
contribution
jujubes
litany

There's a pause while Ernest finds the definitions for three of the words, copies, pastes, and sends. He's shaking his head as he sends the next message while thinking, *how things change!*

> **Jujubes are hard candies that look like small gumdrops. I used to get them at the movies when I was a kid. I bet you could find them on-line.**
>
> **-------**
>
> **thanks gramps**
> **happy reading**

Ernest closes his laptop and takes his grandson's suggestion, quickly finding his place.

> Only moments into their next coaching session, Faddiest was riding about on a shiny blue unicycle. Surging forward, then backward in damp earth, he carved out a deep, plump, capital letter U. Putting the final touches to it, he recited words he'd read earlier on a website, "The unicycle became a fad in the 1920s. Taken up as a hobby by thousands of people, it has also been used in entertainment shows. Recently, however, it has been found to have beneficial qualities including a reduction of stress and an increase in mental capabilities."
>
> "So, a unicycle has more that one purpose then, right?" asked Jump.
>
> "Yes," said Tode, "it gets people around in a fun way; it's entertaining to watch as someone rides; it seems to be therapeutic; and there's one other purpose it will serve for us today—it will take us right into U."
>
> "Into me?" asked Jump, surprised.

"Well yes, . . . in fact, we will be getting more deeply into you," said Tode, "but I was referring to the letter U—the first letter in the word unicycle and the second letter in . . ."

"My name—Jump!"

Tode nodded. "Yes. U, the second letter in J-U-M-P stands for 'Understand Everything'."

"Everything?" said Jump with awe. "That's a lot! How will I ever 'Understand Everything'? I only know about the nighttime marsh, and of course, now I know a few things about colorful dreams and 'Justify Nothing', but I don't know where to start with 'Understand Everything'."

"Swim over here, near the damp shore where I've carved this letter U,' said Tode, "and put yourself right inside the letter." Faddiest made a little channel from the main pond so that Jump could swim right inside the U.

Jump slid into place. Turning to face Tode who had hopped off the unicycle right at the base of U, he heard, "Good," as Tode continued. "Now we could say that you're inside of U, right?"

"Ha, ha," said Jump, catching the joke. "You're teasing me."

"On the contrary," said Tode. "I'm illustrating a point: that to 'Understand Everything' we begin inside the letter U, or as you said before, inside you. 'Understand Everything' is a very tall order as you have noted, so we're going to break into halves. Look to where the down stroke of U lies next to the red jump rope J we made before. That U down stroke is

the first half of 'Understand Everything', and it fits right next to 'Justify Nothing', which is where?"

"Inside me!" said Jump.

"Right," said Faddiest, "and our intention in the first half of 'Understand Everything' is to learn who you are inside and how you operate; to Understand Everything—Inside Yourself."

Jump's eyes noticed that the down stroke of U was beginning to fill up with water from the channel Tode had made. Continuing to trace the letter's shape with his eyes, he looked to where the up stroke lay carved—deep, wide and dry in the marsh bank.

His curiosity prodding him, he asked, "What is our intention for the second half?"

"When we get to that, our intention will be to help you 'Understand Everything' about how you interact with the world around you," answered Faddiest, "and if we do our homework in the first half, learning to 'Understand Everything' about the inside of you, we will have much more wisdom to bring to the up stroke side where you 'Understand Everything' about your relationship to the world. Put the up stroke and the down stroke together, and you 'Understand Everything—About Yourself.'"

There are two parts of the U in J-U-M-P.

The first part is the down stroke: Understand everything inside yourself.

The second part of U is the up stroke:

Understand everything about how you relate to the world outside of you.

"Now," Tode went on, "I emphasize the word 'Understand', because even if you lived for a thousand years, you couldn't come to 'know' everything there is to know about yourself, but you can most assuredly come to truly 'understand' what you do know much more fully, powerfully, and wisely. You see the U in J-U-M-P is the landscape between your private inner world of 'Justify Nothing,' and the public world outside of you that asks you to justify everything. Without a strong U between the J and the M of J-U-M-P, it's easy to lose your way."

"What's M?" asked Jump.

"That's what everyone wants to know," answered Faddiest his eyes twinkling and his head swaying back and forth. "They look to the outside world without first understanding that what they see there is greatly influenced by the eyes they use for looking at it. If

U

the eyes are looking through confusion, what they see will be distorted."

Jump swam to the down stroke edge of the U where the water was filling deeper and deeper. He peered in and was amazed to see a tadpole face looking back. "Who is that?" he asked.

"Who, indeed!" said Tode. "That is the question of the day. For starters we could say, 'It's you', my young tadpole. It's your reflection looking back at you, and over the course of the next few weeks, we're going to examine that reflection. We're going to look at it through bright eyes, and tired eyes, and thoughtful eyes, and bold eyes. We're going to find in there, what really excites you in life, and discover your unique purpose. We're going to examine your personal boundaries and personality preferences, and come to 'Understand Everything' about the beliefs you hold and the habits you've formed. We're going to learn about the things that really matter to you, your personal values."

And so it was that Uncle Faddiest Tode led Jump into the world of self-reflection, each day offering him a new lens through which to see himself. Some lenses, Tode called 'assessments,' some 'inventories,' and some just 'exercises.'

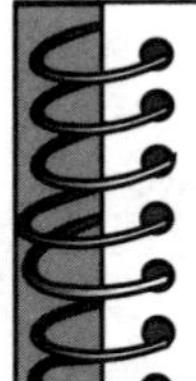

Look at who you are through a number of different lenses.

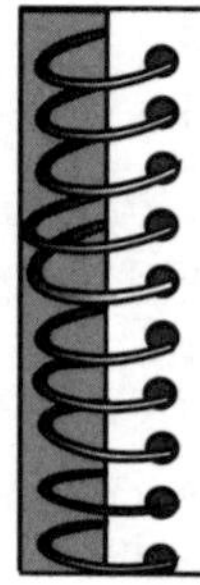

Use the mirror and the microscope to view the details of who you are before you use the telescope to look out onto the world.

Answering questions he'd never thought to ask, Jump learned that he had values and beliefs that formed the foundation of the way he saw the world. He was, in Tode's words, 'value-based.'

"Those who are not value-based," said Tode, "are more prone to 'justify everything' inside themselves. With no understanding of the values that drive them they don't have the strength of character to champion their unique and special qualities."

"That's sad," said Jump.

"It is sad," agreed Tode, "and it is also dangerous because it is the full expression of unique and special qualities that brings a sense of vitality to the processes of daily life. Creatures who are not aware of their values don't take very good care of themselves. They are the ones who suffer burn-out at work, because they become overrun by the needs and demands of others."

"Values," said Jump, setting the word in his mind.

"It is a word that has almost lost its meaning," said Tode ruefully, "because it has been used and abused until creatures see it or hear it and say 'ho

hum.' But, values are essential to the choices we make in life. Like the paint on a canvas, our values hold the colors, and form the shapes of all of our thoughts. If we blindly go about life without knowing what our values are, it's like letting others paint the painting for us."

Exploring his personal values was particularly intriguing to Jump. Tode prompted him to sort out the things he truly cared about all by himself from the things he thought he "should" care about because others had said so.

"From your unique values," said Tode, "you will forge your 'non-negotiables.' They are the things that matter to you so much that you simply will not engage in activities where they are not present."

"Non-negotiables," said Jump. "Like what?"

"Well," said Tode, thinking of an example, "an important non-negotiable for you right now is that everything you do is to be done very near the marsh because you are presently dependent on the pond water to catch your breath. When your lungs are fully formed, you may decide to change that non-negotiable, but for right now, it is a condition you must honor and insist that others honor as well."

"I don't think I ever would have thought about that," said Jump.

"We often overlook our non-negotiables," said Tode, "either because they are so basic to who we are that we assume others understand them, or because we haven't focused on discovering what they might be."

With Uncle Faddiest leading the way, Jump learned that he had a unique balance in the way he perceived the world around him. Like most frogs, he enjoyed the touch of a thing, its sight and sound, but the sensate details of the world took second place to the dreams and visions that filled his head. Most often he was guided by a kind of 'sense' of things.

"It's called 'intuition'," Tode told him.

> What really matters to you?
>
> Do you trust your intuition?
>
> What are your top ten values?
>
> What are your non-negotiables?
>
> How do you take in and process information?
>
> What is your purpose in life? In work?

Weeks passed and Jump's body began to change. Where once he had resembled a stubby nosed fish, now, his hind legs were budding, strong and true, and there were little bumps just behind his jaw that would soon be the front legs leading him to land. Breathing easily in the water through his gills, he also learned to

exercise his lungs as they formed.

A metamorphosis was happening inside too. With Tode's help, Jump identified parts of himself in the infinite diversity among his frog kin. Bullfrogs, green frogs and tree frogs are different in how they communicate, the habits they have, and the things they care about. None are right, and none are wrong, just different. Seeing this helped Jump to better 'Understand Everything' about his own ways of being, thinking and acting. Learning more of 'who he was', he came to appreciate the unique ways in which he saw, heard and felt the world around him, and this understanding helped him to see how 'who' he was greatly influenced 'how' he was in the circumstances of his life.

Carefully examining his unique passion for the flaming orange hoop, Jump began to glimpse the purpose that was driving him to it—his own unique reason for being alive. He increasingly sensed it had something directly to do with making Bold Moves.

Each week Jump spent some daytime hours with Tode; he then worked to apply what he learned to his activities in the nighttime marsh. But as time passed, he found himself drawn more and more to the bright colors of day. His nighttime world grew shorter until he found himself seeking his bed on a regular basis just after midnight and waking on the early side of morning.

Meanwhile, the big letter U Faddiest had carved on the marsh bank deepened and widened, filling more fully each day with water until the bottom of the letter lost its outer edge completely to the greater waters of the marsh, and the up stroke, which rose to slightly higher ground, grew damp and a bit soft.

Somewhere between the U and the M of J-U-M-P, you start noticing a change within you.

Ernest closes the book, reaches for his phone, and punches in Joe Putnam's number for their scheduled coaching call. "I'm thinking," he says moments later, "that most "movers and shakers" have a pretty strong bias that says they already know themselves very well."

"That matches my experience in coaching," Joe says. "I find that clients who see themselves high up on the ladder of success are more resistant to the possibility that there might be things about themselves they don't yet know—the higher up they are, the more resistant. This means that when they take a leap of faith, they're likely to end up in Brash Move territory. It's interesting what happens, though, as they begin to see that most, if not all, of the perceptions they have about themselves are based on messages from the world outside. When we start exploring their world inside for authentic clues and answers, Brash Moves fall away, and Bold Move opportunities become more and more apparent."

"At the risk of sounding like one more out-of-touch client," says Ernest, "I believe I've been very fortunate in that regard.

I became fascinated early on in life with questions about my own nature. In fact, I had difficulty fitting in with my peers as a child because I was distracted—wondering what makes people tick, myself included."

"I hear you," says Joe. "You're definitely unusual in that way. It's like you explored the landscape of U all by yourself. However, in the weeks we've worked together, I've asked you to take a number of self-assessment inventories and it seems to me that you've learned many new things about yourself."

"Oh yes," Ernest responds, "You've helped me get a lot more specific in my understanding of who I am and what I care about. Before—working without you—my passion for environmental advocacy was there in a feeling sense, but it wasn't clearly defined in practical terms. Now, I understand more about what drives me forward and how to manage myself, even in the most difficult moments."

"Great," says Putnam. "So when you find your leaping frog, you'll have the first hand experience needed to mentor your frog into similar self-awareness, which is what the landscape of U is all about.

"Speaking of leaping frogs," says Ernest, "I land in Kalamazoo in a few hours to meet with a woman named Evelyn Dodd. She's done some innovative things at our arena there, but frankly, we don't hear about them until months after the fact."

"Kalamazoo," Joe says, masking his surprise. "Evelyn Dodd, you say. And you think she might have a shot at being your jumping frog?" *Stay very neutral here, Putnam*, he thinks to himself, catching up with this news. *Stay very clear and absolutely professional.*

"That's right," says Ernest. "I've only met her briefly a

time or two, but the reports I've gotten indicate she has great intuitive insights. She just doesn't fully trust herself until she's certain she's hit a home run. I'm concerned that there's too much self-protection going on there for a jumping frog."

"Hmm," says Putnam, reserving direct comment. "I wonder what kind of a B word Faddiest Tode would apply to the moves she makes."

"Well, they're much more than Barely Moves," says Cottingham, "certainly not Brash Moves, but definitely not deliberate, Bold Moves either."

"How about Background Moves?" Joe offers, making them both laugh.

"That'll do," says Ernest. "I just wish I wasn't feeling like she might be my frog of last resort."

"It's important to have patience, here," says Putnam. "It's most likely that the frog you're looking for hasn't had the benefit of experiencing the J and the U of J-U-M-P. You can't expect the Optimal Operating State to be in place. There may not be conscious awareness of the attitudes, beliefs, and values that are motivating action. If your frog is making Background Moves, a sense of purpose may be only vaguely formed. If your frog possesses the passion to make a Bold Move, it is likely to be raw, undirected, unmanaged."

"It's easy to forget that," says Cottingham, "especially since I'm just getting some conscious competence in those areas myself. It's like when I read Jump's story, I see myself as a kid, fighting all of my Inner Critters, but somehow I managed to put them into perspective."

"Some kids are blessed with a greater ability for self-reflection than others," says Joe. "Like other natural Bold Move makers, you were one of them. There was a series of shifts that happened as you navigated the territory of J and U. Starting in J with curiosity, you moved to self-reflection in U, and somehow, probably with the aid of encouraging adults, you massaged that self-reflection with self-knowledge until you gained ownership of your strengths. That gave you the confidence, self-esteem and deeper wisdom needed to make Bold Moves."

"My dad used to sit with me at bedtime and ask me what I liked and didn't like about the person I'd been that day. Did I like how I acted? Was I proud of my work? Did I take time to play?"

"Your dad was a natural coach," says Joe. 'You were extremely lucky. He was helping you learn the art of self-reflection and it sounds like he was also teaching you how to 'be.' I'd say he was giving you his version of the Whisperer Log we've talked about, where you keep a record of the mood-changing events you experience each day, and the self-reflective insights that help you recognize your sense of fulfillment."

"Making notes in the Reader's Log is like that for me," says Ernest. "I find that I'm recognizing a lot of jewels in the Jump story, subtle lessons that might easily go unseen."

"How might those notes be helpful when you finally find your frog?"

"I suppose they will help me in my role as a Bold Moves mentor," says Ernest.

FOURTEEN

Global Thrills Family Arena, Kalamazoo, Michigan

After ending the call, Joe Putnam flips his cell phone closed and Jackson Ulysses McPlayer palms his computer mouse to prepare for the coming performance. These two actions, so closely juxtaposed, highlight the different roles he currently plays in relation to Global Thrills, Inc. His ethical standards as a coach have him reconsidering those roles, given the unexpected fact that they will soon collide right here in Kalamazoo. *I'm doing a very subtle dance here*, he's thinking, *poised between Ernest and Evelyn. As Joe Putnam, it's my job to make sure Ernest has the support he needs in his search for the frog that's ready to jump out of the pot. I didn't feel any need to tell him of my alternative identity as one of his performers before now because I had no sense that it was relevant. I'll have to let him know about Jackson as soon as is reasonable.*

As Jackson McPlayer, I've got to hold steady in my resolve to push forward with my Bold Move in today's performance. I owe that to myself, and until this moment, I hadn't dreamed it might intersect with Ernest's process. But with my Bold Move providing a challenge to Evelyn, I've landed right in the middle of his search for the jumping frog.

If Evelyn can get on board for my Bold Move, it might be just the evidence Ernest needs to identify her as his jumping frog. As her friend, I'd love to see her make a Bold Move here too. There's a part of her that knows my Bold Move is viable, but it is essential that whatever she does today, she does in her own way for her own good reasons.

Clicking to check off the final item on his pre-performance list, Jackson releases the mouse and pushes back from his control console. Everything is in order for the matinee and he has several hours to rest and relax before his performance. Integrating upgrades is always a challenge for him. Having spent most of the morning practicing with the bike, he thinks to himself, *It's going to be so fun, making this change. I can't wait to see the audience response!*

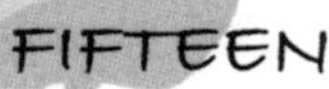

FIFTEEN

Global Thrills, Inc. Corporate Jet,
Somewhere Over Utah

Ernest takes Joe's advice and records in his Reader's Log, some notes from the coaching call.

In the U of J-U-M-P, you establish your foundation:

- attitudes
- beliefs
- values
- desires.

You define your purpose and discover the core of the passion that motivates you.

In the J, there is curiosity.

In the U, self-reflection leads to self-knowledge and ultimately to ownership of your natural and gifted strengths.

U

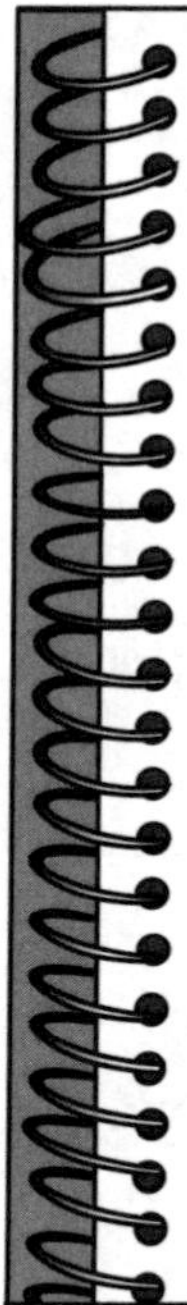

Then confidence and self-esteem kick in and you're ready to make a move.

Keep a Whisperer Log where you record those moments when you take charge of your mood by replacing Critter messages with Whisperer messages.

Reflect at the end of each day how well you held your Optimal Operating State that day.

Returning to the book itself, he's thinking, *I'm recognizing lots of things I already know, but the book is providing insight into how my experiences have contributed to who I am as a Bold Move maker.*

The water of the marsh felt like silk on Jump's skin as he glided effortlessly between clumps of tall grass. All the bright colors of his day were settling into familiar shades of gray with the coming of twilight. For weeks he'd felt like an explorer on safari in the exciting outback of a foreign land. So many insights came to help him 'Understand Everything' about himself from the inside out. So many fresh sights, sounds and smells helped him rediscover the world around him in accord with his own unique way of being and seeing. Birds he'd known only by their night calls flashed brilliant feathers under the sun of day: blue on jays, flashy gold on finches, and red on cardinals so bright it nearly glowed. Wing by wing, they added to his faith that somewhere in the rainbow of creation he would find the flaming orange hoop and the raspberry red Star Dude suit. He felt so good, so very good. Never before had he known the water in just this way. It was neither warm nor cool, but matched exactly the in-between temperature of his skin. *Like I'm feeling the world from the inside out,* he thought to himself, *like the marsh is matching up with me . . . a true reflection of all the things that make me as I am.*

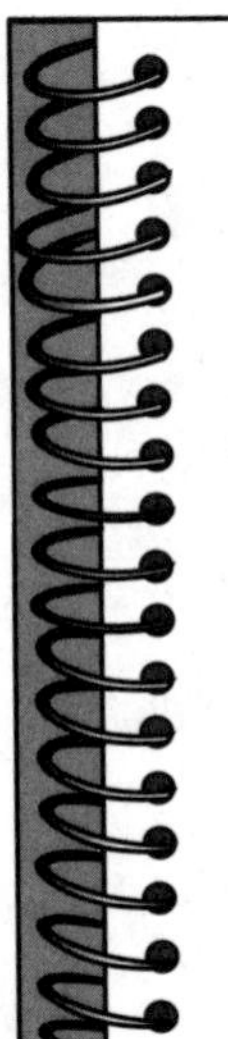

The down stroke of U fosters the self-knowledge needed to confidently access the sense of "being" that underscores your Optimal Operating State.

When you start accessing the "being "state in the being/ doing conversation, there's often a sense of amazement.

Jump's mind skipped back a few weeks to the image he'd seen of himself in the watery down stroke of Tode's unicycle U. He had a sudden urge to see

it again. Seconds later, peering in, he was startled at the changes in his outward appearance. His head had a finer shape, eyes popping up in a most impressive manner, and where there had once been tiny bumps, he saw front legs forming. *I'm different*, he thought, *from who I used to be*, and he remembered too, how different he was from the other Fogg family frogs. Instead of feeling odd about it as he once had, he felt confidence, even pride, in his uniqueness. *Learning to 'Understand Everything' about who I am is very exciting*, he thought, but before the words could fully settle in, he spun about, tail brushing through the mud of the marsh bank, and found himself strongly drawn to the unexplored up stroke side of the giant letter U. *Now I want to 'Understand Everything' about my relationship to the world outside of me.*

Pause to reflect on your deeper values and . . .

Get a higher level of confidence to meet the outside world . . .

because you are accepting yourself more intentionally.

Thus, assume greater ownership of your unique strengths.

Calibrate Bold Moves readiness by noticing how clearly you can see your true self in the outside world.

The U in Jump builds a protective shield through which you can view external influences

Accept or reject them as is appropriate to what you know about who you really are.

Due to subtle erosion over several weeks of time, the up stroke side of the U was awash in water that had seeped from the bottom of the letter where it was open to the greater body of the marsh. It wasn't clear or reflective like the down stroke. Instead, it looked brown and dull. Still, the mysterious surface had a strong power of attraction, and Jump found himself peering in more and more deeply. Searching for his

U

reflection, all he saw was a long, faint shadow of his frog head cast on the muddy surface by the late afternoon sun.

That's odd, Jump thought. *When I look into the U's down stroke and see the inside of me, I seem to 'understand - pretty much - everything', but when I look into this part of the U that shows me my relationship to the outside world, all I see is my shadow.*

Just then, a voice he hadn't heard in some time sounded inside of him. Only the size of a whisper, it said, *Once the lessons of 'Understand Everything—inside yourself" are complete, you will be able to see a great deal of yourself reflected in the world around you.*

As quickly as it came, it was gone, drowned out by a loud Inner Critter voice shouting, *You'll never learn all the 'inside' lessons. Better jump into the outside world while you still can, and sink or swim!*

Unable to resist the pull of the unknown, Jump did just that. Plunging into the muddy up stroke of the U, he held his breath against the sand and silt in the water and swam about not seeing a single thing. In the murk, he was swept away by the gentle current that drained water down into the bottom part of the big letter. From there, he washed out into the marsh itself where the water finally began to clear. *So what's the big deal,* he thought to himself, *it's the same old marsh.* But, swimming about, greeting other creatures—some going to sleep and some just waking up—he began to see there was something subtly different about the place. The grays and browns looked grayer and browner. Resisting the onset of evening, Jump thought about the joys of his day.

"You won't believe the colors of the birds," he yelled just moments later when Plop's head surfaced after her first dunk of the evening.

His sister rubbed the water from her eyes and peered through the glaring light of day. "Bird colors," she said. "I've seen 'em. There's a gray heron right over there."

"Oh," said Jump, nearly swimming right out of his skin with a need to let his sister know, "there's so much more than gray in the world. There's red and bl - - -", but Plop was gone, diving down, then breaking the surface again and again to practice her plop, plop rhythm. She woke up a caddis fly larva and a tiny isopod. Soon her plops would be big enough to wake even owls.

Suddenly Jump felt alone. He'd actually been alone for hours enjoying the colors of afternoon, but he hadn't noticed his aloneness at all. Yet here, in the dimming light of his most familiar neighborhood, he did notice. *You're alone because you're acting badly*, said the Critter voice inside him. *You should be practicing too, learning to jump high enough and loud enough to wake up the creatures of the marsh. Why, you've wasted weeks chasing rainbows.*

Just then, Jump spied Skita Fogg skittering her floppy frog feet to splash water across the marsh banks. It was her job every evening, to wake up thousands of fireflies sleeping in the damp soil. See, said Jump's Critter voice, she's doing what she's supposed to do. Look how hard she works. You should be ashamed of yourself. And for much longer than a moment, a very ugly feeling overtook the tadpole. The Critter words went on and on. *You let Skita down and Dermand too. They don't deserve to have such a lazy son. You're nothing but a dreamer!*

You can master your inner Critters internally and still fall prey to them when influential external images and messages are imposed upon you.

To make himself feel better, Jump crawled up onto a floating log. There, as the misty grays of the marsh grew deeper, he mustered all his strength and made the highest, longest jump possible for a tadpole that still had a tail. He was instantly rewarded, because when he landed, a loud thonk drummed up from the log's empty innards and roused an entire hatch of damselflies. They rose up dancing like fine ladies at a society ball. Jump watched them swirl, almost in a trance, until his father's voice broke his concentration.

"Pretty good, there, Jump. I bet if you tried again you could wake up that gaggle of geese," he said pointing across the still marsh surface.

Jump's mind leaped from damselfly magic to try, try again, just as the word, "Okay," popped out of his mouth. "I'll try from up there," he said looking up at a branch of the log hanging out over the water. "A cannonball should do it."

And indeed it did. Once he climbed to the top and leaped off, his splash not only sent the geese flapping, it drenched his father who laughed a deep Dermanding laugh and patted his son on the back more than once.

"We've missed you," he said. "Your mother and I were worried when we found you sleeping late last night. Are you sick?"

"No," said Jump. "No, I'm just fine, only . . . "

"You'll be losing that tail soon enough, son," said Dermand not wanting to hear any excuses. His laugh dried up into stern, serious advice. "And then your work begins in earnest. You should put in a few extra hours of practice tonight. You've got a lot of making up to do."

Making up to do, thought Jump. *Yes, you should make up your practice*, echoed his Critter voice. The tadpole looked about as the light faded, and he couldn't help admitting that the day did indeed, seem to be just ending. The sun was nearly gone, the just-at-sunset breeze was finishing its rounds, and the day creatures were heading for hollows and holes. He thought of his cozy waterbed, but he didn't want to disappoint Dermand or make him angry, so he pushed on with all his remaining strength and jumped about in the misty gray. Up and over and around and aside he jumped at a steady pace, waking up an impressive number of small fish, baby birds and insect larvae.

One jump landed him atop a beaver lodge, rousting out everyone inside. *Gee, this isn't so hard,*

Jump's mind told him, but as gray marsh turned to black, it did begin to feel hard—not in a physical labor kind of way, but because a dull sameness set in that made his heart grow heavy. Still he jumped and jumped, making up for time lost in dreaming.

On the way to making Bold Moves, some activities, and even some people, will be identified as counterproductive.

These will be given a different priority or they will fall away entirely.

The marsh went from gray to black. Stars grew brighter and brighter, then dimmer and dimmer again. On the eastern horizon, the hazy pink glow of almost morning rose up just in time to make a striking silhouette of Dermand who was posed on the bank getting ready to call the end of night. A series of plump balloons bulged out right under his chin and collapsed again trumpeting solemn frog songs into the coming dawn. The first of these was enough to stop Jump in mid-leap. *He's Dermanding,* thought the tadpole, *in no uncertain terms, that work stop at once. He's saying it's bedtime for the night creatures. Period.*

And that means you too, Jump, said the Critter urging him off to bed.

Sleep was a welcomed friend to Jump that morning after a half day with Faddiest and a whole night practicing his jumps. He dreamed of Dermand saying, "Good boy. Good job. That's what we like to see. Practice makes perfect!" But just before noon, his dreams turned cruel and he saw himself trapped in a slithery slick of stinky pond scum. When he tried to swim away, his tail got tangled up in awful rotten things. When he tried to jump out, his feet slipped and the scum grabbed him back like mummy fingers covered in sticky glue. He kicked and struggled with all his might, but the only thing that changed was his fright— it grew bigger and bigger.

> The power of the Inner Critters can show up in the subconscious mind, in dreams.
>
> Before you go to bed, lock and load your Optimal Operating State by writing in the Whisperer Log.

On the marsh bank nearby, Uncle Faddiest was reading the *Atlanta Daily Star*. His concentration was interrupted by a ruckus on the water—Jump seemed to be thrashing about in a wrestling match with a lily pad. Though he was a dry land creature, old Tode sensed he'd better hop in and see what was going on.

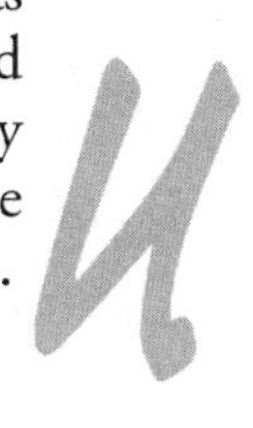

"Whoa there, son," he said, calming the tadpole as he fought his nightmare. "Wake up now. You're okay, you're just fine."

"What?" said Jump. "Oh, thank heaven, I was only dreaming."

"Come settle yourself a moment," said Faddiest. "You've had quite a fright."

In the shallows near the shore, Jump's heart slowed down to its normal amphibian rate. The midday sun was warm and inviting. He watched two dragonflies dart about together, nose to tail. *Their blue is so electric,* he thought. *I do so love the daytime colors.*

Without missing a beat, his Critter voice yelled at him inside his head, *You're a nighttime frog. You should learn to love the misty grays of the marsh after dusk. Better go back to sleep—save your strength, you're going to need it. Practice makes perfect after all.*

Because he was concerned about the little tadpole, Faddiest was closely monitoring the changes in Jump's expression and he knew at once what was happening. "This message is partly true," he said in response to the unsaid thoughts. "Practice does make perfect, but what your Inner Critter hasn't said is that it is extremely important to practice the right things in life."

"But how do you know what the right things are?" asked Jump. "Is it right to be a nighttime frog and practice jumping like everyone says? Or is it right to be a daytime frog like you say, and learn about new things?"

"Oh," said Tode, "I believe you've misunderstood me. I've never said it's right to be a daytime frog and I would certainly never say it's wrong to be a nighttime frog. Both are exactly right when that's the kind of frog you truly are. Your job is to figure out your own unique brand of frog-ness."

"But I get so confused," said Jump. "My dreams tell me one thing, and my family tells me just the opposite. Some of my thoughts tell me this, and some of them tell me that, and I don't know who or what to believe. . . and you keep saying it's all up to me!"

"Yes," said Tode, "it's up to you to 'Understand Everything' inside so that when the outside world gives you messages you have a way of measuring which ones fit you and which ones don't."

"What about the messages I give myself in my inside world?" asked Jump. "Like the Critter thoughts in my head? I don't think they like me to learn new things, and I don't know how to make them go away."

Perfect, thought Tode. *It's about time we talked more about those.* "I can help you with the Critters," he said. "In the landscape of Justify Nothing, you learned how to identify your Inner Critters so you could know at any moment who had the microphone in your head. Here, in the landscape of 'Understand Everything', you must learn to manage the Inner Critter voices so they can't prevent you from livingyour life with passion—from your own unique purpose. Come with me and we'll learn more about them." U

Once again, Ernest sets the book aside and e-mails Ernie:

Hey guy, how's it going?

----

okay i guess
i think i have inner critters :(

Me too sometimes. Need help?

----

want to do my homework? :)

It sounds like your critters are trying to keep you from learning. Something very similar is going on for Jump. Are you to that part of the book yet?

----

past that part

going now mom's coming

Check in later and tell me where you are. Maybe we can talk on the phone sometime soon.

----

ok bye

SIXTEEN

Global Thrills Arena, Kalamazoo, Michigan

Evelyn likes her place in the sun. Though she demonstrates the guts of a prizefighter to her staff, she is not into taking big, public risks, and she's extremely uneasy about what Jackson is calling his Bold Move. To make matters worse, the media has somehow heard that something's up and press vans are arriving in droves.

How did this happen? she asks herself. *How did I miss seeing that I was heading for disaster today? I'd just like to run away.* If asked about the water in the pot in which she is swimming, she will undoubtedly report it is beginning to get stiflingly warm.

Feeling the need to do something—now—to cool things down, she tries to reason once more with Jackson.

"You've filled the place every time you've been here," she says. "Why fix it if it ain't broken? I know the thrill seeker entertainment game, and this scheme of yours won't fly! People like being fooled. You've had them eating out of your hand."

Jackson grows quiet inside himself. He connects with his Optimal Operating State—his place of clarity, comfort and ease. "It sounds to me like you're afraid," he says, presently, "that if I try something new, you'll embarrass yourself in front of your boss."

"Not on your life!" says Evelyn, jutting out her chin, "I'm a 'no fear' kind of gal. You just don't know this business the way

I do. You've gotta zero in on what works. Why, I've made more money the last five years than Madison Square Garden! I'm at the top of my game for Global. Doing everything right!"

"Is it possible that contracting with me has been part of the reason for your success?" asks Jackson. "You've had an exclusive contract with me for three years now. We have both profited from that. Is it possible you could just trust that booking me for this performance was the right thing to do? That in some subtle way you knew what you were doing?"

"I don't know," says Evelyn, hesitantly. "Nearly everything inside me tells me your new stunt is too risky."

Jackson—or maybe it is Coach Putnam—can't resist probing deeper here."Everything inside you," he says. "So what exactly do you know about what's inside you?"

Evelyn accepts the challenge. "I'm a winner," she says. "Everybody knows that! I know how to get things done in the thrills business. I understand everything about it, the machines, the people, the box office, concession sales; you know . . . everything."

"So when you say that everything inside you tells you my new stunt is too risky, the 'everything' you're talking about is your rapport with your performers, your understanding of their machines, and your ability to relate to customers, juice ticket sales, and buy and sell merchandise, right?"

Defensively, Evelyn says, "Yah, that's right. I know myself pretty well. I like what I see and so does corporate."

"Yes," says Jackson, "but you're missing my point here, because none of the things you mentioned: machines, people, customers, concessions—or corporate—are actually inside of you. Are they?" And gently, respectfully, he continues. "They are all outside of you," and just above a whisper, "aren't they?"

The tone of Jackson's voice doesn't soften the blow; Evelyn is stunned by his words. Forehead pinched in the middle, she stares at him blankly.

"You see," he says in a wise tone very much like that of a certain sage, old toad, "you've learned how to adjust very well to the demands of your job, to your whole work world, actually. You're very, very good at what you do, and your boss loves you, but . . . and I've known you a while now, . . . I've never seen you excited about work. You're upset half the time and just about to fall asleep the rest of the time. Bored out of your mind is how you appear. Then there are those times when you worry.

"I say there's fear behind that worry, fear behind that upset, and fear even, behind your boredom. I say you don't recognize that fear. I say you don't understand much about who you are on the inside. Not really."

Evelyn's lightly rouged cheeks grow purple and quiver. Not saying another word, she leaves, shaking her head with studied jerks. Jackson is a big money maker for Global Thrills, and Evelyn doesn't have a clue about how to rein him in and maintain the good will needed to keep the act.

Jackson smiles a knowing smile and let's it go. *It's going to be an interesting afternoon!* says a voice in his head—a strong, solid, 'understand–everything–inside–me' voice that first spoke to him years ago—as just a whisper.

SEVENTEEN

Global Thrills, Inc. Corporate Jet, Somewhere Over Kansas

Cottingham fingers his bookmark and checks the previous page of the story, rereading how Tode is about to give Jump a lesson in managing Inner Critters.

> Still getting his land legs, Jump followed along after Tode as best he could, his tail still dragging in the mud. He was anxious for help with his Inner Critters. When they reached Tode's nook, he sat Jump down amid his pile of books and tapes and said, "Just check these out for a few minutes while I set us up for an experiment."
>
> Jump shuffled through the pile looking at titles: *The Seven Habits of Highly Successful Frogs*, *Do What You Love and The Minnows Will Follow,* and one he especially liked called, *What Color is Your Parrot?*
>
> "There are many good steps, tips and tricks in that pile," said Tode as he set his Hi Fi on top of an old TV set. "There will be a time soon when you'll want to get into some of them. Good stuff, very good stuff! Couldn't be where I am without them."

Many excellent resources have even more value and impact when you know who you are and your Optimal Operating State is in effect.

Soon Faddiest had gathered up a number of the media fads in his collection and wired them together with a maze of adaptors. Among them were: an old tube-style Zenith® TV, a super eight reel-to-reel Kodak® home movie projector; a Lear® eight track tape deck mounted in a '66 Ford® dashboard; a Walkman®, a ghetto blaster; an old 45 rpm record player, and an ancient RCA® radio.

When everything was ready for the exercise to come, Tode positioned Jump in the center of the hodgepodge of electronic devices with two microphones and a video camera in front of him.

"Now," he said, "I want you to speak into this mic on the right here, and tell the story of what happened to you last night."

Jump told how he was drawn toward the up stroke of the U and saw only his own shadow there. "That's when The Whisperer talked to me. It said that when I learned all the lessons of 'Understand Everything' on the inside of me, I would be able to see myself in the world outside of me too. That was cool!"

The ear membranes on Tode's head undulated

with interest. "We haven't heard much from The Whisperer, lately," he said. "Good to know it is waking up. Just for the sake of our exercise, I want you to repeat The Whisperer's message by talking into the other microphone, the one on the left."

Jump leaned into the left mic and said, "When you've learned all the lessons of 'Understand Everything' on the inside of you, you will be able to see yourself in the world outside of you too."

Then stepping back from both mics, he said, "The next thing I heard was a Critter that said, '*You'll never learn all the inside lessons. . .*'"

"Hold on," said Tode. "Speak the Critter messages into the right microphone.

Leaning in to the right, Jump repeated, "*You'll never learn all the inside lessons. Jump in and sink or swim!* That's why I dove in." As he spoke, a grossly distorted picture of his face appeared on the old Zenith TV and the words *you'll never learn, you'll never learn* rang out at him from the Ford dashboard's eight track tape deck, getting louder and louder with each repetition of the phrase.

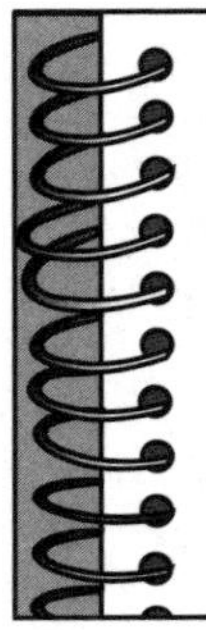

If you jump too soon into the up stroke of the U . . .

you don't bring a clear sense of self so everything you experience there is clouded.

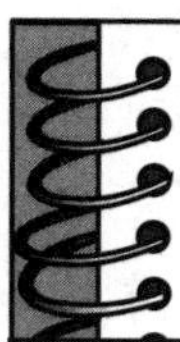

Inner Critters thrive in murky waters.

"What happened next?" asked Tode.

"Well, after I washed out into the marsh pond, I saw Plop and tried to tell her about bright colors. She wouldn't listen, and then I heard, '*You should be practicing too. You've wasted weeks chasing rainbows.*"

Three more TV sets came to life, each with a differently distorted version of Jump's face. The words *you should, you should* growled forth as the boom box fired up, and *chasing rainbows* peeled out derisively from the Walkman.

Faddiest urged Jump to continue. Eyes strained, head shaking against the noise, he yelled into the right mike, "Then I saw Mom skittering on the shore and heard the words, *Look how hard she works. You should be ashamed of yourself.*"

Several more ugly tadpole mugs appeared on various movie screens and computer monitors. A ghetto blaster and three record players joined the other audio voices shouting out, . . . *ashamed of yourself, ashamed of yourself, ashamed of yourself.*

As Jump's story continued, every screen in the hodgepodge came to life with Critter versions of his own face, and every audio player repeated his Inner Critter messages, talking over each other from all directions. The volume got louder and louder until Jump couldn't hear his own words, much less his

thoughts. He stopped talking and looked to Tode for help, but Faddiest just sat there grinning back until Jump finally yelled. "Stop it! Stop the noise!!"

And it did. It stopped. And Faddiest said calmly, "You see?"

"See what?" said Jump. "That I'm as ugly as a slug in every size and shape! And that the dumbest things come out of my mouth?"

Tode was amused. "No. See how loud and obnoxious those Inner Critter voices can get when they see you trying to change? And—and this is the most important part—see how you can shut them up if you just decide to take charge?"

"Wow. I do see," said Jump. "That was horrible!" Then, with a snap of his fingers he continued, "But they went away like that when I said stop. I wish I'd done it sooner. My ears are still ringing from the noise!"

"Saying 'stop' to your Inner Critter voices is very effective. And it gets more and more effective as you practice, but before you can practice saying 'stop', you have to be certain that what you're hearing in your head is in fact, an Inner Critter voice."

"How can I know?" asked Jump.

"Remember," said Tode, "all Inner Critter voices have one thing in common. They are associated with fear. Look for messages that make you feel afraid or those that make you feel guilty or ashamed. It is appropriate to feel those things if you've harmed someone in some real way, but often feelings of guilt and shame are messages of fear in disguise. They can be expressions of your fear of doing something that will make you look silly, or fear of being punished for doing something someone else doesn't like. When Critter voices come up, very often what you're actually doing is merely thinking about trying something different than you've tried before and there's a part of you that's afraid you might fail."

"Doing something different like when I look at the daytime colors? Or let myself spend time dreaming? Or just 'being!'"

"Yes," said Tode, "none of those activities cause harm to anyone or create trouble in the world, so why should you feel guilty or ashamed for doing them?"

"I didn't," said Jump, "until I jumped into the up stroke of U, 'Understand Everything—about my relationship to the world outside of me.' Then all the fear messages spouted off."

"Right," said Tode. "But actually, jumping in proved to be a good thing because it gave you an opportunity to learn important lessons about the down stroke of U, 'Understand Everything—inside yourself."

Jump was listening very closely, trying to follow Tode's line of reason. "Like how loud my Inner Critter voices can be?"

"Yes! And what else?"

"That they only show a distorted version of me? Like the weird pictures on all the screens?"

"Exactly, and one more very important thing . . ."

"That I can shut them up if I want to!"

"Bingo!"

"They get louder and louder, don't they?" said Jump, "the more you explore and change."

"They do," said Tode, "just like all these noisy gadgets. They grow in power and volume as the moves you contemplate get bolder and bolder. We might also say, 'the bigger the brain, the bigger the Critters,' because a highly intelligent frog mind can think of a zillion reasons to stay stuck."

The brighter the brain, the more diverse and sophisticated the Inner Critters will be with their arsenal of negative messages.

"When your Inner Critter voices start increasing in volume, they provide you with a powerful opportunity to take control of your destiny. Critter messages are like a dark drug that takes you into a story of fear, like your nightmare. When you confront them and tell them to be quiet, you can change your story to a positive one."

"Do the Critters ever go away for good?" asked Jump.

"No," answered Tode. "But they do lose their power when your Optimal Operating State gets dialed in because you can readily identify who has the microphone in your head, your Critters or The

Whisperer. Then you change the story by taking control, and it's like turning off the noisy gadgets here, until only one remains—one scratchy old phonograph record that has no real influence over you. That's when you have the kind of control needed if you are to make Bold Moves."

Critter volume can be good news--evidence of your progress, because the closer you get to making a Bold Move, the louder your Inner Critters become.

"Bold Moves are tricky," said Jump. "Was jumping into the murky up stroke of the letter U a Bold Move?"

"No," said Tode. "It was a Brash Move, something you did without consciously choosing to do it. You let your curiosity get ahead of you, just a little, when you turned to look into the up stroke, and then you let your Inner Critter voice trick you into leaping into the murk when it said, *You'll never learn all the 'inside' lessons. Jump in and sink or swim!* As though there was no other possibility."

The dejected look on Jump's face prompted Tode to continue, "But don't feel bad about it. Frogs make Brash Moves all the time and very often there's an Inner Critter voice involved. You see, Brash Moves are often made in reaction to what I call 'triggers.'

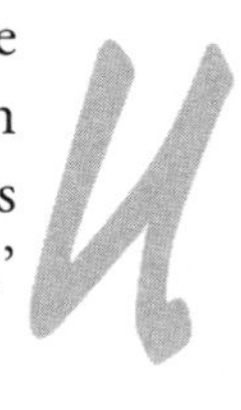

Triggers are sudden fears that jump up inside—fears about things like missing out, losing time, or looking like a wimp. And, fears as we have learned, are the motivators behind Critter messages."

"So, in order to 'Understand Everything—about my relationship to the outside world'—the up stroke of the U—I need to understand what makes me afraid," said Jump. "And be able to identify the Inner Critter voices that remind me of my fears, and remember to say 'stop', when they try to take control."

"That's right," said Tode. "Your Brash Move has shown you that you have a fear that you'll never be able to learn all you need to know about yourself. This recognition is what I call *self-knowledge*. The next time that trigger tries to trick you into a brash move, you will be able to identify the trigger and the Critter."

"Noticing triggers and silencing Critters are important skills needed to maintain your Optimal Operating State. They are to the Bold Move process, like the five-pound weights used in the early stages of developing physical fitness. They give you a place to start exercising self-knowledge, so as you move into the landscape of M in J-U-M-P, you will be able to manage your larger fears. At some point, you will master your fears and manage them with ease. That is the conditioning needed for making advanced Bold Moves in life."

"Boy, there's a lot to learn about making Bold Moves," said Jump once again.

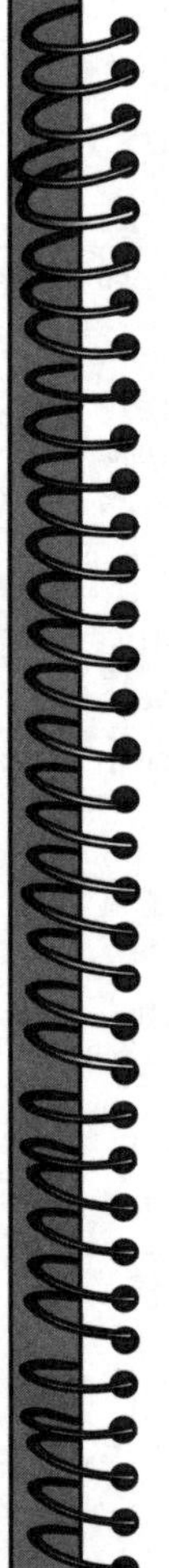

Learn about the "triggers" that wake up your Inner Critters and prompt you to default into making Brash Moves.

Write down your triggers.

Then you don't have to react to them.

If triggers are not written or said aloud, they fall into your subconscious mind and become diffused in your awareness.

There, they lurk, waiting to take you out.

Notice triggers.

Notice that you noticed.

"Yes," said Tode, "and you've learned a lot from the up stroke of the U. I think it's time you looked in there one more time before we move on to the M in J-U-M-P."

Peering in, Jump found himself surprised when he saw his biggest smile grinning back at him. "Hey, now I see myself in the water there," he said as the smile softened into a wistful memory. "It's like when The Whisperer told me I would learn to see myself in the world around me."

Tode tickled a wisdom wart on his left knee. Looking toward the jump rope J on the marsh bank where they had planted their Bold Move seed, he pointed to the sturdy elm sprout now pushing boldly up from the wet earth and answered thoughtfully, "The Whisperer has been here all along. It has helped your Bold Move seed grow like that healthy green sprout there."

"Why is it only a whisper?" asked Jump. "Why isn't it loud like the Inner Critters?"

"The Whisperer always speaks of possibilities and they can be frightening to us," said Tode. "And when we react with fear, the volume of the Inner Critters gets turned up until it is so loud The Whisperer can't be heard at all. If we want to make Bold Moves, we have to learn how to take the microphone away from the Critters and give it to The Whisperer. Otherwise, our Bold Move must wait silently in 'the whisper zone', hoping for a chance to get our attention."

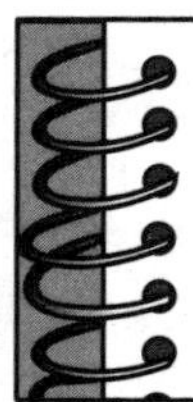

Keep track of your mood.

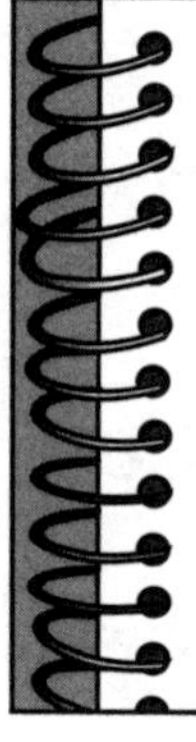

If your mood starts to darken, ask yourself what's going on.

Then your Inner Critters can't gain enough power to take you out!

"So that's why I needed to 'Understand Everything—About Myself,'" said Jump. "The parts that are afraid and want to 'justify everything,' and the parts that are open to possibility."

Remembering how he had dived to the bottom of the pond just weeks ago, to get rich soil for planting the elm seed, and without a cue from Faddiest, Jump dipped his webbed foot into a shallow, still alcove near the marsh bank where rich green algae was growing into a thick, soggy carpet. Capturing some gently in his webbing, he drizzled the algae onto the soil around the elm sprout and smiled at Tode proudly.

"Exactly," said the old one. "Fertilizer! All of the lessons of 'Understand Everything—About Yourself,' all your strengths and challenges, your skills and talents, all your personal preferences, and so much more—add more fertilizer to the tiny Bold Move seed planted inside you. Remember, all the lessons of J and U are meant to help you develop your . . ."

"My Optimal Operating State," interrupted Jump.

U

"Exactly, your Optimal Operating State is coming along nicely," said Tode. "And just like the elm seedling there, your Bold Move has sprouted and is getting bigger and stronger."

"My Bold Move," said Jump, suddenly very serious. "I've been thinking a lot about the possibility of becoming a daytime frog, and the thing is, I think I already am one."

"And how is that?" asked Tode, though he already knew the answer.

"My nighttime world has grown shorter and shorter. I go to sleep just after midnight and wake up to the colors of morning."

"Well," said Tode, "I guess it's official then. You are a daytime frog."

"It's funny, though," said Jump. "I thought that making a Bold Move would feel a lot different. I thought I would decide one day to do it and then just jump in, but it seems like it has happened almost by itself."

Faddiest smiled and said, "Bold Moves come in all shapes and sizes, just like frogs do. The first one often comes gently—like this first one of yours has, because it is a subtle inside move that was needed in preparation for making Bold Moves in the world outside."

As if to illustrate Tode's point, a gentle breeze swept along the marsh bank, stroking the elm sprout that grew inside the jump rope J. Visiting again and again throughout the last days of summer, it would rustle tender leaves, then tiny branches, until at last it brought the chill of fall and turned sapling green to autumn yellow.

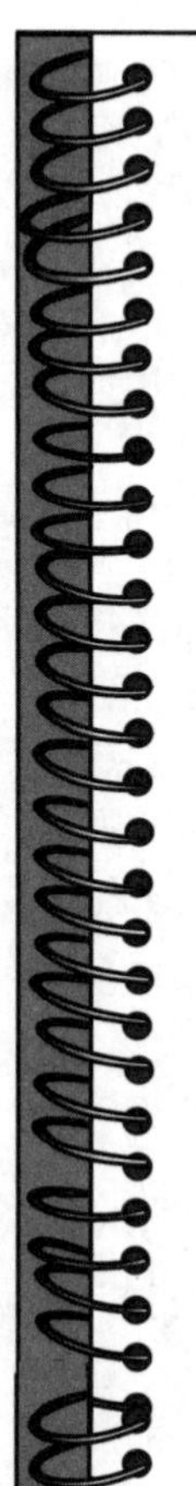

Understand Everything--
About Yourself.

Explore internal terrain
where:

• Individual uniqueness is championed

• Personal challenges are defined and managed

• Unique strengths are fully owned and optimized

• Inner Critters don't have the microphone.

• The Whisperer does.

EIGHTEEN

Kalamazoo International Airport, Executive Terminal

Ernest Cottingham is stiff and sore as he steps down from the Global Thrills Lear™ jet 35. A glance at his watch gives him just enough time to get out to the arena for the meeting with Evelyn Dodd.

He likes what he knows of Evelyn. A capable woman, she is one of only two females in top positions at Global arenas. She had taken some shrewd, calculated risks over the years and pushed her way up. Looking at her numbers, you see a top performer. *She's pretty cautious, though,* he's thinking, *to be my frog that jumps for reasons of her own. She's been a company gal all the way."*

Ernest dials Putnam for one more brief conversation—fresh insight on how to refine his interview process. "The hardest part," Joe says, "will be to stay out of your candidate's way. Allow for a truly independent decision. Your job is to silently represent corporate authority. If your candidate dares to make a move without your express approval—a move that makes good sense—you may have found your frog."

"Should I play out my part and put some obstacles in her path?" Ernest asks.

"Great question," Joe says, respectfully. "It seems to me that you're changing paradigms here, and I imagine that your presence alone could dampen the will of your candidate. Do you want to add to the tension by appearing to be authoritative?"

Ernest laughs. Like most top execs, he isn't entirely aware of the amount of power others attribute to him or the limiting effect it can have upon them.

I'm looking for a Bold Move, he thinks to himself, *just one Bold Move, and just in time for the M of J-U-M-P.*

During the limo ride, he opens the little book once again.

> After long years of exposure to life's miracles, the wisdom warts on old Faddiest's body had learned to play a song or two in celebration of special moments. So he wasn't surprised when the crisp morning air unexpectedly filled up with a joyful noise—the Pointer Sisters singing "Jump — For My Love." *Such energy, such enthusiasm* Tode was thinking. *Such courage*! He flashed on Hugh Grant in the movie *Love Actually.* Hugh was strutting through the halls of Ten Downing Street to the same lively beat—the Prime Minister choosing to engage in his own heartfelt adventure! *It's always like that when the walls of fear and hesitation come down and you just decide to 'go for it'. . . based on self-knowledge.* He shook his shoulders crisply and danced a step or two before remembering that his music played only to his own ears.
>
> Watching, Jump's jaw was on the ground in wonder at the old toad's moves. *Maybe he's got headphones,* he thought, scrutinizing Tode's ear membranes—*and I just can't see them!*
>
> "No," said the sage, mind reading again, "I'm just a bit beside myself because you've already got a solid toehold in the landscape of M in J-U-M-P!

M

"M," repeated Jump, "for 'Move Deliberately'."

"Move Deliberately—Based on Self-knowledge," said Tode.

Bridging between the landscapes of the U and the M in J-U-M-P, they had defined key elements that informed how Jump would relate to the outside world. Examining core values, they identified *honesty* at the top of his list, followed closely by *excitement* of the kind that's involved in high-risk activities. *Precision of action, full self-expression*, and *love of family* finished out his top five values.

Jump's natural skills and talents pointed toward creative use of technology and machinery. And among his *non-negotiables*—those things that simply had to be in place for him to feel passionate about what he did—he cited plentiful time alone to think and create, as well as moments of intense, exciting interaction with others.

Having explored the landscape of 'M' for several weeks, they were putting the final touches to a large mobile in the shape of the letter M. Elaborately constructed of moss and masking tape, it swayed in the breeze suspended by a chain of Mickey Mouse™ watches (spanning five decades) in perfect alignment with the other letters: jump rope J, and unicycle U which had finally dried out with the coming of fall.

"We've been learning together for some time," said Tode, "looking at new possibilities, and exploring different ways of thinking and being. Now it's time for you to make an important deliberate choice. Will you keep looking for the flaming orange hoop and the raspberry rhinestone Star Dude suit, no matter where it takes you, or will you find other ways to satisfy your excitement for colors and dreams within the confines of the marsh."

"But I didn't have to be deliberate before," said Jump, "when I chose to become a daytime frog. Why do I have to be deliberate now?"

"Because until now, everything we've done has been about seeing if you have the ability and the desire to put yourself into an Optimal Operating State for making Bold Moves in the outside world," said Faddiest. "One important reason to develop the Optimal Operating State is so that your Bold Moves can be deliberate, based on your understanding of yourself—your self-knowledge. Before, I could help you in small ways with the 'deliberate' part as your coach because I knew what to look for. Now it's time for you to decide whether you're up for your next Bold Move and, if you are, just what it will be."

There comes a time when making a Bold Move becomes a solo journey.

Success in the outside game cannot depend on direction from a coach or any other outside influence.

"But it's so hard to know what to do next!" said Jump. "I love Mom and Dad, and I don't want to disappoint them by leaving the marsh. I've learned that jumping around in the dark doesn't float my boat, but I haven't told them. What will Mom and Dad say if I leave the marsh altogether? How can I change my life forever and still be a good son?

"What do you think I should do?"

Tode didn't answer. He didn't even blink. He just gazed at Jump with an expression that said undeniably, *You know I won't answer that question.*

"Okay, I know," said Jump. "I have to decide for myself. Only I can know what's in my heart. Only I can know, deep inside of me, my reason for being."

Tode's expression shifted only enough to imply a question; *So how might you proceed from here?*

"I need some time alone," said Jump, recalling how important alone time was to his sense of clarity about things, "to make up my mind."

"An excellent idea," said Tode. "I'll finish this giant M here and meet you in the morning."

Autumn had nature in a state of paradox, with completion on the one hand as nuts and fruit fell from above, and a palpable sense of new beginnings on the other hand, as the languid mood of summer was supplanted by the season's sharp call to attention––the harvest. Heat-loving flies and mosquitoes had already disappeared into dormancy, but furry creatures scurried about, foraging for winter stores.

Jump sat enthralled by the full on, blast-your-eyes explosion of color, color, everywhere. Both annuals and perennials were morphing, some quietly to deep forest shades tinged in blue, and others extravagantly to egg yolk yellow, mango orange, and deep rouge edged in mauve. The warm, heavy marsh mist had lifted, stirred by a thousand beating wings that landed and launched, wending southward. *The water fowl seem so sure of their direction*, Jump thought to himself.

Yah, chided an all too familiar voice, *and you aren't. You don't know what you're doing!*

"Go away," said Jump aloud, "nasty Critter!"

Jump had developed real skill in observing the conversation between his Inner Critters and The Whisperer voice inside him. In Tode's weightlifting metaphor, Jump was now lifting thirty-pound weights as he increased his informed self-knowledge and sustained his Optimal Operating State for longer periods of time.

One of the most important lessons in the M of J-U-M-P was the design and implementation of a daily practice. Each day, Jump made notes in The Whisperer Log. It was a wonderful compilation of his positive inner messages that helped him notice the progress he was making and kept him in an optimistic mood. As a result, he began to hear The Whisperer more and more clearly.

Every morning, Jump set an intention for his day. He imagined himself being in his Optimal Operating State and doing things that moved him toward his Bold Move. Each evening, he would take time to notice whether his intention had come alive in the practical circumstances of his day. He learned to keep a neutral mood about whether they did come alive or not—a mind state that Tode called *staying unattached to the outcome*—but Jump was always amazed and amused when the intention he had set was realized, almost as if by magic.

He regularly practiced changing negative thoughts into positive thoughts and checked, throughout each day, the condition of his Optimal Operating State. At first, his daily practice seemed like a lot to accomplish, but very shortly, Jump realized that it saved him a lot of time that he might otherwise have spent correcting mistakes and recovering from the overwhelming effects of fear and worry.

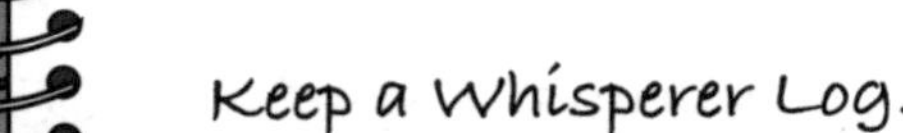

Keep a Whisperer Log.

Every evening, record a log entry about something positive that happened during your day.

This becomes physical evidence that your Whisperer is present.

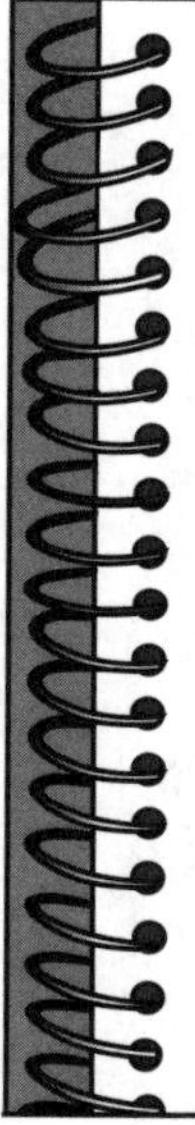

Over time these log entries accumulate as undeniable evidence that The Whisperer is partnering with you in a fulfilling life.

Create an intention for your day by naming a desired outcome like:

"My interaction with others will be clear and thoughtful."

On that autumn day as he took his alone time, Jump was reminded of something Faddiest had said in his lesson about the M in J-U-M-P, "'Move Deliberately' is about choosing. Every choice you make, large or small, makes a difference. Sometimes the most difficult choices are extremely subtle, like choosing to notice when a Critter is trying to get you, and then choosing to silence it."

'In fact', Jump recited in his mind, *'choosing is THE way to make any difference in your life.' I know it's true, but right now choosing a future feels too hard, too big for me.* And without being alert to the fact that he was choosing to divert his attention from the conscious act of choosing, he jumped into bracing water and went for a late afternoon swim.

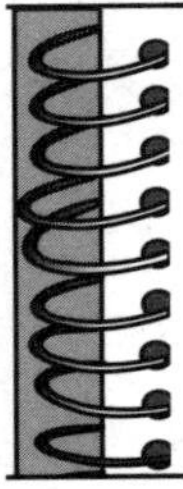

Even not making a decision is a decision. You may think you're not choosing, but you are.

With his tail nearly gone, Jump swam not as a tadpole, but as a true frog with long legs and webbed feet. Effortlessly, he shot through the water, and just as easily, climbed on a rock, a log, or a lily pad only to leap and splash again and again into the cool wet marsh. *I've grown up*, he thought, *inside and out!* And while he knew his body had changed according to nature's plan, he was reminded by a friendly voice that some changes both outside and inside himself resulted from his choices. *Think of the daily practice you've committed to in preparation for your Bold Move. You've strengthened your body through routine exercise*, said The Whisperer.

Swimming about, Jump could feel it was true.

You've been exercising your Optimal Operating State too, it whispered on, *gaining control over your thoughts and actions.*

I guess so, Jump heard himself think in answer to The Whisperer, *but I feel kind of stuck when it comes to moving deliberately. It's so much easier to just wait and see what happens.*

Committed, The Whisperer continued: *You chose to change from a nighttime frog into a daytime frog. You chose to 'Justify Nothing' and 'Understand Everything.'*

And I chose to listen carefully to you, thought Jump, *The Whisperer voice. And now I need to choose whether or not to follow my dreams.*

You are ready. Believe in yourself, said The Whisperer.

Then, right on cue, came the other voice, *If you chase after the flaming orange hoop, you'll lose touch with the marsh,* it warned.

A feeling of sadness gave the Critter new footing in Jump's mind. He tried to shoo it away again, but as the shadows deepened around him, it came again and again, louder and louder.

You'll be all alone out there in the world, and no one will care because you will deserve to be alone.

Only frogs that follow the ways of the marsh are welcomed here.

You'll see. Even Skita and Dermand will turn their backs on you.

"No they won't," yelled Jump aloud, and to prove it to himself, he swam to where his family had gathered on the marsh bank for twilight rehearsal.

At a certain point in Bold Move development, the power of The Whisperer voice drowns out the brash loudness of the Inner Critter voices.

NINETEEN

Global Thrills Family Arena, Kalamazoo, Michigan

Jackson's Inner Critters are raising a ruckus. *There's nothing like a really Bold Move*, he thinks to himself, *to wake up those pesky fellows!* You'll never make it, they say. You'll break your stubby neck—fall flat on your . . . well you get the idea, but Jackson knows about Inner Critters. He knows that no matter how grown up you are, no matter how skilled or smart, no matter how many times you've shut them up in the past, Critters will yell at you louder and louder, the closer you get to making a truly Bold Move.

He knows they are trying their best to keep him from making the move of a lifetime and revealing his secrets to his fans. *You're signing your death warrant. Your career will be over. No more intrigue, blah, blah, blah.* But Jackson measures the messages against what he understands about himself. He has no doubt that the escalating volume of the Inner Critter voices is a sure sign, not that he's about to mess up—a limiting belief––but that he's on to one more big, exciting breakthrough in life.

TWENTY

Expressway to Global Thrills Arena,
Kalamazoo, Michigan

Midday traffic is light as Ernest's limo heads east toward the arena. The ride affords him just enough time to read another chapter of the Jump book while taking a few notes.

> When he arrived at the Fogg family rehearsal, Jump was struck by the fact that he already felt like an outsider. No one noticed his arrival. Plop was busy plopping about in the shallows, Skita expertly slapped and flapped her webbed feet, fore and aft, against the sandy shore, and Croak's eyes were closed, making room for a giant air bubble that was filling beneath his chin.
>
> In his powerful, 'Dermanding" voice, Dad presided over all, saying to each in turn: "Yes, good Dear, good skittering."
>
> "More air, Croak, more air."
>
> "Plop, start your plop from higher ground. Make it a mite deeper for more sound volume."
>
> When he finally spied Jump, Dermand stopped short. Opening in recognition, his mouth could find no words to say and both father and son knew it was because for longer than a month, Jump had focused his efforts exclusively on daytime jumping.

He had quit coming to rehearsals. He had stopped following Dermand's instructions entirely. A taut hush befell them and each looked for a place to lay their discomfort.

"You're late," said Dermand, finally. And Jump didn't know for a second or two whether he was in fact late, or merely absent.

Late, late! said a Critter. *Bad, bad frog. I told you, you wouldn't be welcomed!*

"Faddiest kept me too long," muttered Jump, but even as he said it he knew it was just an excuse, and one of the lessons of M in J-U-M-P stood sharply in his mind. *We make a zillion choices everyday, big ones and little ones, and we never stop to realize that's what we're doing. Then when life doesn't feel good, we don't realize that we've chosen it and we try to blame someone or something in the world around us.*

Can't even remember your lessons! Now you're blaming Tode—shame on you, said the Critter.

But The Whisperer stood his ground. *Just tell the truth Jump. You don't have to justify your choice to focus on your dream, but it would be considerate to share with your family more about what you're doing in the daytime so they have an opportunity to understand you.*

Tell the truth, ha! came the retort. *You don't even know the truth about what you're doing. How are you going to tell it? Besides, it's your dad's fault for being so demanding. He's never understood you and he never will! He's just a Fogg frog from the world of black and white.*

Don't listen to that Critter, said The Whisperer.

Go back to your non-negotiables. No limitations on the colors in your life, remember? Give Dermand a chance. Tell him what you're doing. Right now he feels that you've abandoned him and the rest of your family, because he has no point of reference to comprehend the choices you've made.

What choices? You don't know how to choose!! roared the Critter.

The choices I've made, thought Jump, staving it off with just a flicker of understanding. *I've chosen to stay away from twilight rehearsal.*

Twilight fostered further dawning as the lessons poured in. *I just forgot for a moment that I choose—that every moment of every day, I make choices. I choose whether to get out of bed or not, and what to eat for breakfast. I choose which of Faddiest's fads to explore, what websites to visit, what TV programs to watch, what books to read. I choose my friends and my enemies. I will choose my job soon and eventually, I'll choose someone to love.*

Now there's a rich one!! chided the Critter.

You'll choose who you will love???

I don't think so!!!

Blasting frantically in stereo, the Critter could incite no reaction. Jump had his bearings and he navigated the landscape of M with confidence, the essence of the land strong and steady inside him: Move Deliberately Based on Self-Knowledge. The lessons spelled themselves out in his mind: *I choose even when I don't consciously choose to choose! I am responsible for choosing how I am and who I am in life.*

M

If I'm aware that I'm choosing, I can be deliberate in making my choices. When I am deliberate in choosing, I can be fully responsible and accountable for the choices I make.

These signposts in the landscape of M synthesized into Jump's Operating State all at once and he was able to do something quite extraordinary as he faced his father there on the marsh bank.

"I take full responsibility for giving you the impression that I've chosen to be late," he said. "The truth is, I chose not to come to rehearsal at all this evening. The truth is, I chose to forget all about rehearsal just as I have for some time.

"I came here because I wanted to prove to myself that I still had strong ties to you and the rest of my family. Right now, I can see that my unexplained absence throughout the past weeks has eroded those ties so much that neither of us knows if we can trust them to hold us together."

Skita froze—listening. Plop slid silently to shore—listening. Trying in vain to silence the giant croak that filled his air sack, Croak gulped, burped, and finally stilled—listening.

Dermand, the proud head of the Fogg family household, had a lump of anger lodged in his heart and he didn't know how to manage it, so he scowled. Other eyes popped up from reeds and lily pads as other creatures came to see what the ruckus was about. Dermand saw with embarrassment that they would all witness the ending to the tense drama that stood stubbornly between father and son.

"You've been seeing too much of Old Tode," Dad snapped finally, desperate to excuse the repugnant moment.

"No," said Jump, "the discomfort between us is not Uncle's responsibility. It is mine. I chose it."

Dermand sputtered indignantly, "Well, you'd better choose again if you mean what you said just now, about family ties."

Ha, ha, he's got you now! yelled a Critter.

"You're right," said Jump, staying his course. "In making my choices, I knew there would be consequences, but I couldn't know for certain what they would be. Now I see that while my choices were right for me, personally, my way of handling them has caused problems when it comes to honoring you, Father—you and the family."

Dermand's lump shifted, nudging the walls of his heart and allowing his blood to flow just a little. This made more space, but his eyes defended still, harshly.

"From now on," Jump continued, "I promise to keep you informed about my choices."

Softening fully into Dermand's right atria, the lump transited his heart's receiving chamber, found its way to the nearby ventricle, and broached the entrance to a vein. There wasn't yet, momentum enough to send it on; the way seemed too narrow. Still, an inquisitive flicker of light had his eyes soften their edge.

"I won't be coming to rehearsals anymore, Dad," continued Jump, "but I want very much to spend

M

time with you and the family in other ways if you'll allow me to."

The impact of Jump's words soothed Dermand's pulmonary valve, activating a gentle kneading motion that dissolved the anger lump completely. It washed out into his veins, indistinguishable from his life's blood. The accompanying rush of oxygen had his head swinging from side to side in awed surrender. The eyes, at last, melted and moistened.

Jump moved closer and closer in a mood of respect, until his arms reached for Dermand in a hug.

"Where have you been?" asked his father. "I've been worried sick."

"I'm sorry, Dad," said Jump, blinking now to keep unwanted drops from falling. "I've been in a different world, and I want so much to tell you what I've been doing, and why."

By taking full responsibility for the choices he had made and by continuing to honor his choices with the help of The Whisperer, Jump had unwittingly opened a channel of love—a connecting link to his father that stripped away the power of his Inner Critters.

Ernest pauses. He sees in Jump his own commitment to family and to complete, honest communication, even when it is challenging. Gratitude for his father's wise mentoring wells up as he readies his pen. *This story highlights important keys to the process of choosing what he always called "right action." Hmm . . . so the rightness of the action, or move, comes from inside—Move Deliberately Based on Self-Knowledge.* The many notes that follow, though sparked by the story, draw also from this natural Bold Move leader's own experience.

Bold Move choices are above the radar.

They are connected to your value system and to your personal energy.

Bold Move choices have a charge to them because they incite the conflicting voices of your Inner Critters and The Whisperer.

Once the charge is directed toward informed deliberate action, the heart can open in new ways.

Bold Move leadership requires clear, complete communication--

-- so that others can understand and participate in the Bold Moves process.

Scowling, scolding, and blaming are ineffective responses when you hold a position of leadership.

You become like an Inner Critter.

Bold Moves are discouraged by such behavior.

Your willingness to be completely responsible for your choices---

--is the integrity that's available inside when your Optimal Operating State is in good order,---

---and you know who you are.

That integrity is essential to winning the inside game.

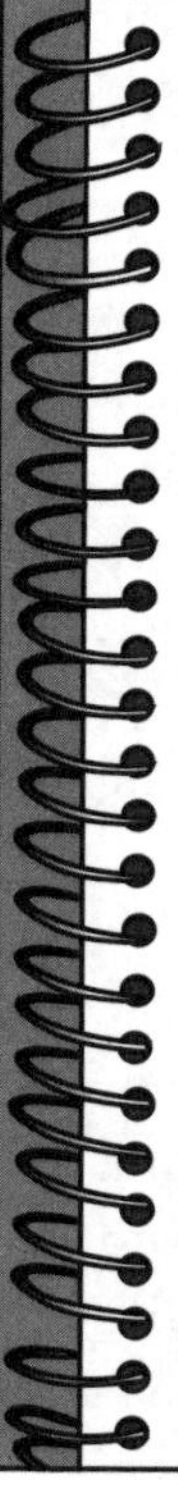

You choose even when you don't consciously choose to choose!

You are responsible for choosing how you are and who you are in life.

If you're aware that you're choosing, you can be deliberate in making your choices.

When you are deliberate in choosing, you can be fully responsible and accountable for the choices you make.

That night, there was a very small campfire in the marsh, with stories told from the world of rainbow colors. The Fogg family was amazed to learn that one of their own had become a daytime frog. They listened intently to all of the possible meanings for the letters J-U-M, and they made Jump promise he would teach them about P, too, when he'd learned all of its lessons.

Croak was particularly interested in Jump's ideas about choosing and being deliberate. "Makes sense," he said, "but if what you say about choosing is true;

if I make zillions of choices everyday, and if I stop to be deliberate about every choice I make, I'll never get around to choosing, will I?"

"There are lots of choices that only affect your life in small ways," said Jump, smiling and echoing Tode's words, "like what you have on a given day for breakfast, for instance. If you eat something that makes you sick, you'll learn from it and choose something else the next day. It doesn't take much thought to figure that one out. But over many years, if you want to be a healthy frog, you'll learn to be deliberate in choosing healthy foods."

"So being deliberate is more important when it comes to bigger choices, is that it?" asked Croak.

"Yes," said Tode, "the more a given choice impacts your life, the more carefully you will want to think about it before choosing and making your move. And when you contemplate making a truly Bold Move, it's most important to be very deliberate."

"So it won't be a Brash Move," chimed Plop, showing her command of a prior point in the lesson.

"Yes, good," said Jump. "Most creatures are completely unaware of the profound impact their choices, large and small, make in their lives. That lack of awareness about choices leads to confusion and Brash Moves. Even when it seems like we have no choice. . . like being born into the nighttime marsh . . . we still choose how we will act and what we will think about our situation. Being deliberate is when we do something on purpose . . . after thinking about it carefully and thoughtfully. Deliberate choice is what Bold Moves are made of."

Dermand was a bit nervous about all the talk of Bold Moves, and choosing and change, but Skita reminded him he couldn't hold the tadpoles back from their destinies.

"It was your wisdom as Jump's father," she said, "that sent him off to find Uncle Faddiest and his hoops. That was a Bold Move for you to make and it was the beginning of your son's Bold Move process."

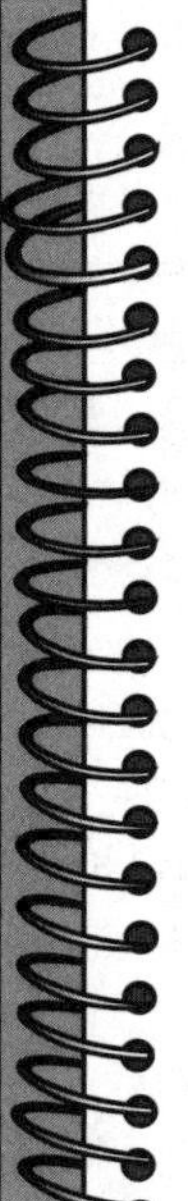

There is a moment in the Bold Move process when it's clear that something new is happening.

This "something" often recalls a prior moment of insight.

It is proof of the power of intuition as a starting point, and the value of The Whisperer as a guide.

TWENTY-ONE

Global Thrills Family Arena, Kalamazoo, Michigan

Jackson's pre-show energy is heightened when Evelyn Dodd returns, bringing in tow four members of the Global Thrills Board of Directors as well as the CEO himself, Ernest Cottingham. There is a collective swagger to their stride as they approach. *They understand their power,* Jackson muses, *and I've got a challenge on my hands.*

Evelyn makes brief introductions all around. Disguised in his helmet Jackson is thinking, *It's just as well my voice is camouflaged by this helmet. I'm sure Ernest wouldn't recognize my face, but my voice is familiar to him. What a pickle I've gotten into here! I've got to just be Jackson McPlayer for now. The right time to reveal Joe Putnam will come soon enough.*

"We know you're not a company man," says Evelyn, taking the lead without further pleasantries, "but surely you can understand our position on this. We're asking you nicely to reconsider this new stunt."

"I do understand," says Jackson, his words sounding strangely electronic through his helmet's speaker, "better than you'd care to know, I suspect. But the bottom line is, we have a signed contract giving me the right to design my own performance. I'm fully insured, and there's no direct liability for you."

"We know you can take care of yourself," counters a board

member, "but you're messing with a winning formula. That's what Global signed for."

Jackson nods his head thoughtfully. "Perhaps we might look more closely then," he says, "at my winning formula."

"It's clear," says Evelyn, posturing, "you wow the fans with daring stunts!"

"Hmm," says McPlayer, "it may seem that the secret to my success is the daring in my deeds, but it isn't actually the level of risk in my act that keeps fans coming back. Lots of riders do far more dangerous tricks than I do. In fact, to be honest, my stunts are intrinsically not very risky at all. They are founded on precise technology and executed very, very deliberately.

"No, it isn't the risk in my moves that keeps them coming back—not even the impression of risk. I've learned over the years that fans come out again and again because I always have something new for them, something unexpected. My moves are bold because they are original and creative—entirely unique to me. My daredevil image is just a mask I wear because it gives people a comfortable way to relate to me, a sense of the familiar. But the true appeal of what I do rests in who I am, someone who is fully expressed!

"When people witness someone being entirely who they are—full on, no holds barred—they secretly want to have a little piece of that person because it is basic to the nature of living creatures that we yearn to express what is most unique and authentic about us. The way fans get a little piece of me is by buying tickets and banners and mugs, and by sitting in the stands to watch what I do."

Each Global board member wears a different brand of astonishment as they listen to Jackson's words. Never has anyone made such a blatant pitch for individualism in their combined corporate presence and they simply don't know what to do.

Jackson pauses. Looking steadily at Evelyn through the reflective visor of his helmet, he sees the woman who helped him break into the thrills business, the person who has become his friend.

Caught like a herd of deer in headlights, the members of the Global Thrills, Inc. Board of Directors are united in what they do next in response to the conflict between Evelyn Dodd and Jackson U. McPlayer: they look to Ernest Cottingham, CEO, with a singular question in their many eyes: *What should we think of this?*

Cottingham is silent, but his mind is creatively engaged. *What the heck's going on here*? he's thinking. *I've heard about this Jackson guy. He's got the Bold Moves intelligence, all right. Could it be that I am actually looking for one of our performers? Someone from the outside?* The excitement of hearing a kindred soul espouse the very Bold Moves principles he'd been learning for many weeks spins Ernest around pretty good, but in the end, he reconnects with his prime directive. *My frog has got to be someone from the inside, not a loose cannon who is clearly doing his own thing.* With laser beam clarity, Ernest Cottingham, CEO does what he has come here to do. He surveys Evelyn Dodd.

Evelyn is visibly cogitating quite deeply on the thread of truth in Jackson's words. Brow knitted, lips pursed, she perceives for the first time two distinct compartments in her brain: one part for personal thoughts where ideas about being unique and fully expressed make complete sense to her, and another part for corporate thoughts where such notions have never before seen the light of day.

"Can you say more?" she asks peering deeply into Jackson's visor with an expression of sincere curiosity.

Come on Evelyn! Jackson is thinking. *Go for it!*

"You see, for most people," he says, "being fully self-expressed is only a dream, one in which they dare not believe. Instead, they 'go along' to 'get along', never acknowledging the dreamer that lies within them. As a result, their interaction with the outside world is timid instead of bold. So when they witness someone making a Bold Move, they think, *How wonderful! I wish I could do that.* To my fans, I'm a Bold Moves expert, a deliberate perpetrator of the unexpected. And today is my day to make the Bold Move of Bold Moves!"

"I see," says Evelyn, suddenly recalling the many moves she has made in her day to get where she is. *But my moves have been carefully calculated to please 'corporate,'* she's thinking. *I've never actually made a Bold Move of the kind that Jackson's talking about. I've never really taken a risk, however calculated, simply because it felt like a perfect expression of myself. Maybe Jackson is right. Maybe I don't know myself well enough to make a Bold Move deliberately and wisely.*

She looks at Cottingham for a cue. His gaze is steady—no discernable expression on his face.

Good job, Ernest, Jackson is thinking.

Evelyn feels herself sitting on a balance beam with the possible collapse of her career on one side and an opportunity to do something remarkably bold on the other. Her mind shifts from thought to thought. *I do basically trust Jackson. He's always come through in the past.*

Is Cottingham testing my judgment here? Or is his silence an indication that he doesn't have a big problem with this?

Why should he? He doesn't know what Jackson is really up to here and this is not the time to try to explain all of the complexities involved.

I guess I'm on my own with this decision, in full view of the big decision makers.

If I'm really honest with myself, I have to admit I'd love to see Jackson's Bold Move.

Then she hears his words repeat in her head, *"The true appeal of what I do, rests in who I am, someone who is fully expressed!"*

I wish I could be fully expressed here, she muses, and suddenly, her mind clicks into a deep, surprising calm.

"Okay," she says finally, "let's see how this plays out. Go on Jackson, make your Bold Move."

"I feel confident you will soon be glad for your choice," says McPlayer, revving his engine.

"Locked and loaded," he yells, over the noise. "Now, please excuse me, I have my final prep to do."

TWENTY-TWO

Skybox, Global Thrills Family Arena, Kalamazoo, Michigan

Ernest Cottingham is in a very good mood. He's pretty sure he's found his jumping frog, but he will see the afternoon through before approaching Evelyn Dodd on the matter. It's enough for now that he's given her Bold Move a meaningful nod and excused himself, leaving her to manage the run up to the matinee. With an hour to wait, he's found a quiet corner where he reads more pages of *Jump.*

> Faddiest wasn't the least bit surprised the next morning when Jump reported, "I know what I want to choose. I choose to seek out the flaming orange hoop and the raspberry red Star Dude suit no matter where it takes me . . . And . . . I choose to be the best son and brother I can be, while still being me."
>
> "Bravo!" said Tode, supporting Jump's cleverness. "You've seen through the illusion of black and white, either/or thinking and realized that you don't have to choose between two things you really want. You can open your world wider, let the rainbow of possibilities in, and deliberately choose both!"
>
> "Hey," said Jump, feeling pretty proud, "I didn't think of it that way, I just knew I couldn't stop exploring and I couldn't stop caring about my family!

Then, I realized that I had already chosen both. I don't know how I'm going to make myself happy and make time for them too, but I know I have to try."

"You've made a very powerful deliberate choice, Jump," said Tode, "and I am certain that if you stay open to possibilities, your choice will lead you to the flaming orange hoop and the Star Dude suit of your dreams. And I know you'll find ways to also honor the life you're leaving behind. You're ready for your next Bold Move." *I wonder what it will be?*

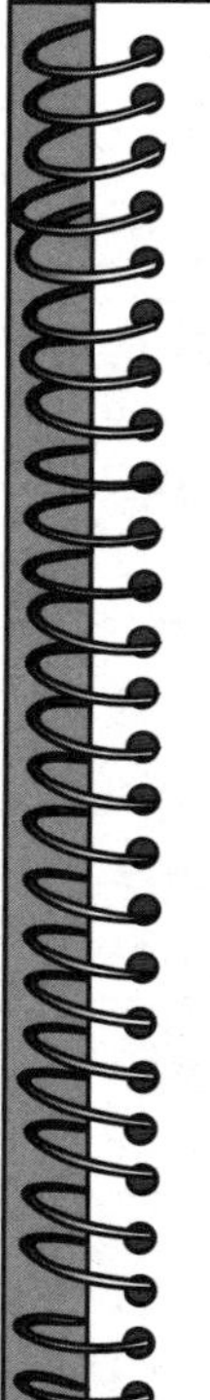

Bold Move territory is not limited to either/or, black/white thinking.

It is available in all the colors of the rainbow.

Bold Move territory contains ideas and actions of many subtle hues, tones and values.

The weeks that followed found Tode coaching Jump through the process of being very deliberate about discovering his next Bold Move. Based on all of the things they had come to know about him, they mapped out an action plan calling for the young frog to spend a month or so exploring possibilities with a focused intent on finding the flaming orange hoop. Though this was a fairly broad and somewhat open-ended goal, they agreed that it allowed for the development of intuition as well as logic, and maximized Jump's chances of creating a direction that was truly new, and aligned with his unique, pioneering nature.

His life purpose, of course, had something to do with jumping. With Tode's help, he came to understand that by jumping he could become a model for others, and maybe not just for other frogs. Other creatures too, might see him jump through the flaming orange hoop, just as he had in his dream, and be inspired to try new things in their own lives. Tode cautioned him, though, that jumping through a flaming hoop was often used as a metaphor for taking any kind of bold action, and that his destiny might not include an actual ring of fire. It might just be symbolic of another feat he would perform. This insight became especially important as Jump's legs developed, because though they were amply strong and adequately formed for nighttime marsh work, they seemed a bit too thin and stringy for the kind of dynamic jumping his imagination craved. So it was, that he began looking for models. What kind of jumping would he do? And where?

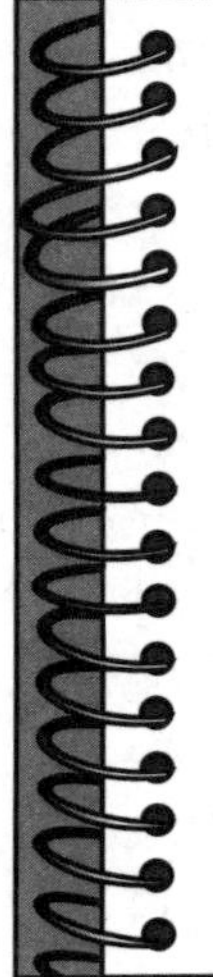

Choices become deliberate when they are measured against in-depth self-knowledge.

The M of J-U-M-P is informed by the U: Move Deliberately--Based on Self-knowledge.

Jump studied the jumping of kangaroos, rabbits, crickets, and fleas, but found no real inspiration. Faddiest brought out an endless stream of jumping fads: pogo sticks, trampolines, even a pair of homemade "spring shoes" he won on E-Bay®. Some of Tode's contraptions added to the height and strength of Jump's jumps, but none generated enough speed and daring to match the ones in his dreams.

Late fall summoned basketball season, a jumper's paradise. Hopping and hitching rides for two days, Jump ventured for the first time into the world of people. He went to Atlanta to catch the Hawks™ at home. Near a puddle outside the dressing room, post game, he closely avoided being squished by paparazzi rushing to cover the first win of the season. He decided that even though he loved the energy of the sports arena, basketball would never be his game.

I'm an introvert, he thought to himself, *and a thinker. I much prefer my time at the computer working out math problems and dreaming up inventions. But what does that have to do with jumping? I could invent jumping aids, but the thrill in that would go to the customer, not to me.*

> In designing a Bold Move, it is important to be realistic about your strengths and your challenges.
>
> Be clear about your individual preferences.

Meanwhile, inside his head came a steady stream of comments from the Inner Critter gallery. *You'll never find your destiny,* they said. *See, we told you: you should be jumping in the nighttime marsh. You were born to it! You're only wasting your youth on impossible dreams.*

"Go away!" Jump would say, and they would for a time. Consistently rejecting them, he stripped away some of their volume and power, but they were persistent, waiting for those moments when the young frog was particularly vulnerable.

Faddiest was there at every turn, mentoring and coaching Jump through his exploration, reminding him of his non-negotiables, and guiding his management of the Critter voices. At times the mystery of Jump's destiny and how he would find it puzzled them both, but the old master knew about how to hold steady in the chaotic questions of personal evolution and change.

"The discomfort you feel is creative tension," he would say. "It's just raw energy you can direct toward any end as long as you don't let the Critters feed on it. Brush them off, keep your mind open and let your intuition guide you. You'll figure it out."

The Optimal Operating State must be tended and reinforced at every step into Bold Move country to avoid infestations of Inner Critters.

The Optimal Operating State is supported by intuition, imagination, and openness to possibilities.

Remember The Whisperer Log, a place to record the physical evidence of magic happening.

It was on his return trip from the Hawks game that the first light bulb went off—quite literally.

Riding atop the MARTA shuttle from Philips Arena to Five Points Station, Jump saw the flaming orange hoop, huge and bright: the logo on a neon sign that read, *Lights On Institute*. Below, was a simple web address that Jump set to memory.

"Well, well," said Tode on hearing the news, "the first real bite in your Bold Moves fishing adventure!"

Accessing the website from one of Tode's computers, Jump's excitement exploded. It turned out that *Lights On Institute* was a technical college specializing in software design, and Jump's frogmouth watered as he reviewed the on-line curriculum.

"I believe you've discovered your next Bold Move," said Tode in a very serious tone.

"Going to school?" asked Jump. "But how will I afford tuition? Will they even admit a frog?"

"The Bold Move you're considering is something much more demanding than finding the answers to those questions," said Tode with unusual gravity. "In order to attend *Lights On Institute*, you must become part of the world of humans."

"But I already did," said Jump, "When I went to the Hawks game."

Tode felt a bit of pressure to perform adequately in the coaching moment before him. What Jump was contemplating was a huge choice and an extremely Bold Move for a frog. Only a few had ever attempted working in the world of humans, and while a handful of those had become famous, even the most successful among them were aware that being green in a human world was not easy. The fates of many more had been horrid and swift. Still, Tode didn't want to fan the flame of fear that Jump had worked so hard to extinguish.

"Hitching a ride on a human bus into Atlanta for a day is one thing," he said. "Living and learning among humans everyday is quite another. They can be wonderful heart-felt creatures, and they create magical things, but they are so busy going about their lives that they don't notice details that become critical to creatures like us."

He was thinking about the growing threat to the very existence of amphibian life on earth. *Over the course of my life alone, I've seen several species of frogs and toads disappear right here in Metro Marsh. Research has shown me that the global decline of my close relatives is directly proportional to an increase in human activity on earth.*

My concern isn't just for the occasional small creature crushed while crossing the road. No, humans are spraying the land with chemicals, exterminating what they call pests, and fertilizing their food supply. They don't seem to realize that those so-called pests are food for creatures like us, or that chemical fertilizers end up in the waters of marshlands, rivers and seas poisoning our greater food supply and causing us strange mutations, illnesses and death.

And that is only half the matter; there's the damage humans do to the natural world by thoughtlessly using it as a dumping ground for waste matter of all kinds, polluting all regions and all spheres—land, air, and water.

It would require a frog of exceptional skill and

talent just to survive in the world of humans; for Jump to thrive there would be a miracle, indeed.

But Tode did not assume to know Jump's destiny. His job as a coach was to help the young frog find that for himself, and embrace it fully. So he closed his eyes and took his mind right down into the cells of his wisdom warts seeking the right words to say. There, inside the 360 million year old chain of his amphibian DNA, he saw that if a frog could truly gain the full attention of enough human beings, he might be able to contribute in some small way to the welfare of his amphibian cousins. If that frog could touch the hearts and minds of people, if he could learn to partner with human beings, he might draw their attention to the deadly details they tended to overlook.

In a moment of sheer evolutionary fervor, Tode had an inspired insight: *A frog who is bold enough, smart enough, and creative enough might remind the human race that it is the most brilliantly innovative species ever known, and that it is capable of devising remedies—phenomenally quick and potent remedies—for all that ails the natural world. That frog might be the catalyst for a reversal of fortune, not just for amphibians, but also for all living things on planet Earth.*

Could Jump be such a frog? It was not for Faddiest to say, but the vision he had seen brought him to a deliberate Bold Move choice of his own. If when he opened his eyes and looked at Jump, he saw the high degree of passion he knew would be needed to make a Bold Move of the caliber that Jump was contemplating, he would do everything in his power to support Jump in entering the world of humans and finding his success there.

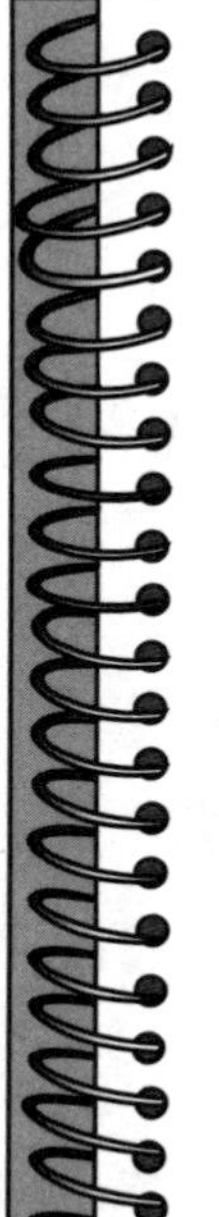

No matter how clearly he might perceive a possible Bold Move . . .

. . . a skilled coach will not assume to know what the client's Bold Move might be.

Rather, he will hold firmly open, the window of possibility . . .

. . . and support the Bold Move maker in making deliberate choices.

When Tode opened his eyes, he couldn't miss Jump's excitement over the thought of attending *Lights On Institute*. It was not only visible it was palpable. Old Faddiest thoughtfully nodded, slowly parted his broad toad lips, and said, "If any frog can do it, you can Jump, but let's not have your excitement carry you away. Let's be very deliberate about your Bold Move."

The magic of Bold Moves has it that once a

true destiny is broached with care and intelligence, the force of providence comes in to open unexpected avenues for success.

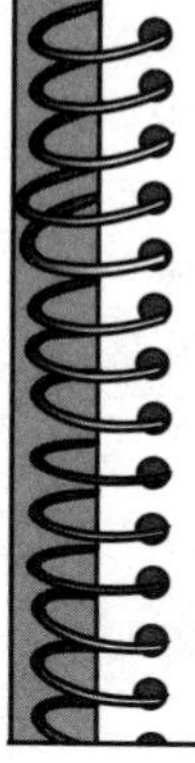

Bold Move deliberation must focus first on the deeper, more internal questions of self.

When those questions are answered, all of the surface questions will resolve themselves easily.

Faddiest and Jump examined the notion of entering the world of humans through each and every detail of Jump's self-knowledge. His Optimal Operating State was reviewed in depth. Skill after skill was surveyed and measured for a good fit. Every non-negotiable was reviewed to make sure that Jump would be able to sustain the excitement he felt once the real work of becoming a part of the human world began in earnest.

It turned out that his application so intrigued the admissions department at *Lights On Institute* that they referred it to Research who invited Jump to become their first amphibian student—on full scholarship. He let them know of course, that among his non-negotiables was an absolute ban on animal testing, so an agreement was struck that required him to take only the standard exams needed for graduation.

"That's how it works," said Tode, not even trying to hide his glee. Leaping high into the air for emphasis, he swatted the giant letter M and set it to swinging. "When you learn how to manage your Inner Critters, listen to The Whisperer, take the time to truly know who you are, and choose deliberately what has heart and meaning to you, amazing—almost magical—things happen. You are ready to make your Bold Move and enter the world of humans."

> Once a Bold Move is deliberately, intelligently set into motion . . .
>
> . . . based on accurate internal research . . .
>
> . . . new possibilities and surprising resources appear in support of the effort.

There on the marsh bank, in the curved part of old Tode's jump rope J, fall had visited the tender oak sapling. First it had turned the few small leaves from green to red, and then it had whisked them away with one brisk stroke of a breeze.

"Look there," said Tode. "Your seed of a Bold Move has grown tall and straight, and it's readying itself for winter. It knows that it needs to go into a dormant state as protection against the unpredictable forces of the winter world that will soon surround it."

"Will it ever grow new leaves?" asked Jump.

"Oh, yes," said Tode. "It is only resting, taking time to think carefully about how it will proceed. Before you know it, the branches will spread even wider and the leaves will spring as if by magic from that silent, solid bark."

"It's like me," said Jump, "resting and getting ready to make my Bold Move."

Move Deliberately--Based on Self-Knowledge

- Venture confidently into external territory
- Engage in highly directed and productive choice making
- Contribute optimally to the world around you.

TWENTY-THREE

Skybox, Global Thrills Family Arena, Kalamazoo, Michigan

The relationship between Faddiest Tode and Jump gives Ernest pause as he reads. He likes to think he is a mentor to young Ernie, or hopes he can be. Reaching for his cell phone, he scrolls down to his grandson's number, and hits send.

"Hi there," he says in a jovial mood, "how're you doing Ernie?"

"I made those Critters shut up," says Ernie.

"Good job," Ernest replies. "You'll be ready for Bold Moves before long."

"Speaking of Bold Moves," says Ernie, "how'd you like the part in the book where Jump shows up late for practice and his dad gets on his case? I wish I could think of things like that to say when Dad gets mad at me."

"You will learn to," says Ernest, raising his voice over the clamor of the arena. "As Uncle Tode says, it's all about knowing who you are and what you believe in. You've got a few more years before you'll be expected to handle yourself as well as Jump did, but I know you'll get there.

"Any new definitions needed?"

"Just a minute, I wrote the words down," says Ernie. "Uh, *providence, palpable, vulnerable, chaotic* and *paparazzi.*"

"Those are good ones," says Ernest. Taking a cue from the Bold Move coaching he'd gotten earlier, he continues, "I'm going to suggest that you check their meanings yourself this time. You can use a regular dictionary, or the one in your word processing program. It's easy to do and getting into the habit of looking up word meanings can be fun. Let me know what you find, okay?"

"Okay," says Ernie. "Where are you calling from, anyway? Sounds like a Global Thrills show going on."

"That's right, I'm in a skybox in Kalamazoo, Michigan and there's an act in the arena getting the crowd warmed up for Jackson McPlayer. His show starts in about forty-five minutes, and he's planning to make a Bold Move."

"That's rad!" says Ernie. "We don't get it 'til later though, and I'll be at the Dodgers™ game with Dad."

"TIVO™ it," Ernest replies. "I think it will be worth seeing." He was tempted to tell Ernie about the other Bold Move he has witnessed—the one that would not be on TV—but Evelyn's story requires too much explaining to be told on the phone to a nine year old. He saves it for later, ends the call, and continues his read.

> Frost crisped the marsh bank and tiny wisps of steam arose from both their amphibian mouths as Jump and Faddiest leapt, squished and pounded to soften, mold and meld lumpy clumps of a dozen different colors. The morning's chill might have daunted them, holding the pliable substance too firm to knead, but where grunts and groans might have been, there sounded only chuckles and satisfied *ahs*, as their rainbow structure received its final touches.
>
> "We'd have a tough time getting this stuff to stay put if it were summer," said Tode. "P makes a tricky

sculpture with this window at the top. The damp air keeps our sculpting material from drying and cracking apart."

Hanging from the backside of the letter's plump upper bulge, Jump popped his head through the window grinning, "This stuff is fun! I love it."

Only a few empty Play Doh™ canisters still dotted the marsh bank, the rest serving as a skeleton for the bright, giant letter P.

"So you see why Play Doh is a fad that's become a classic," said Tode. "It's the perfect substance to form our letter P."

"P, for play," said Jump. "Play to Win." Dropping to the ground in a graceful, young-frog bounce he mimicked the phrase he'd heard from Tode over the past few days. "Play to Win—With Heart and Soul."

"Yes," said Tode, "and coming to the landscape of P means we've just about navigated our entire Bold Moves map, and are coming to completion in our project of finding new meanings for the letters of your name."

"I can hardly believe it," said Jump. "Everything's changed so much since last spring. Life is so different. Like for one thing, I'm not hibernating and it's winter!"

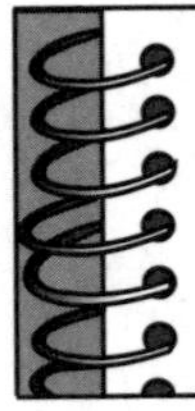

Changing how you know yourself changes your experience of life.

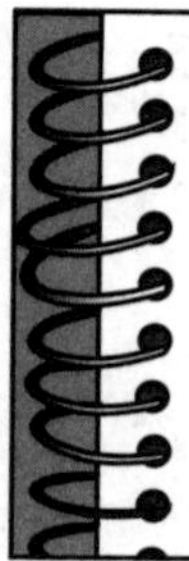

Any need to hide away in self-protection falls away, allowing for new interactions, possibilities and experiences.

The cold was reason enough for most frogs to find a sunny sand bank to burrow into, but Jump found the winter days perfect for his studies on-line. Midway through his first term at *Lights On Institute*, he spent hours each day learning various digital languages and mastering software design techniques. The tail completely gone now, his young frog body was taut and strong by dint of Tode's insistence that he balance his computer time with physically demanding projects like these joyful hours of modeling on a giant scale with Play Doh.

"Play to Win—With Heart and Soul," mused Tode. "Isn't it interesting how effortless life can be when you're living in alignment with who you really are?"

"I just love every minute," said Jump. "Even when I get muddled by my lessons and my Inner Critters try to nab me, they don't have much volume, so pretty soon I'm having fun again—learning. But tell me more about why that is, Uncle."

"Do you remember when we were talking about creative tension?"

"Just before I went to Atlanta and found the

flaming orange hoop on that neon sign," answered Jump. "You said creative tension is like raw energy that can be directed toward any creation as long as I don't let my Critters use it all up."

"Yes, and you've learned to manage those Critters so well, they just don't impact your life as much as they once did. You've become free of the bondage that Inner Critters would impose. Free to direct your creative energy with precision and excitement."

"So it feels easy," nodded Jump, "like playing instead of working."

"And as you know," said Tode, "from watching others in the marsh, most creatures are stuck in a belief that the activities in their lives must be serious. They must be 'work', as in 'work hard.'"

You get callused from decades of believing life has to be "head down, push through."

"Like 'no pain no gain,'" said Jump.

"Like 'I win, you lose,'" said Tode. "And like 'win at any cost!' But when that is the mind set, the cost can get way too high."

"How's that?" asked Jump.

Faddiest dug through his newspaper pile and pulled out an article titled, "A Time to Die." "It says here that in the world of humans—and as you are learning, they are the biggest proponents of the 'no pain, no gain' theory—the most common time for a heart attack to strike is nine o'clock on Monday morning."

Jump measured Tode's words against what he knew of the humans at *Lights On Institute* and said, "When people are starting their work week."

"Exactly," said Tode. "Their hearts are literally breaking at the thought of schlogging in, one more day, to work that is not satisfying."

"So, why don't they change what they're doing?" asked Jump.

"It could be that changing what they do would help, but it's not the answer in itself. As we have seen, the answer has to do with the quality of the state of being one maintains, regardless of what one is doing," said Tode.

"The Optimal Operating State," said Jump, "starting with the J and U of my name, Justify Nothing—Inside Yourself, and Understand Everything—About Yourself."

"Exactly," said Tode, "the Optimal Operating State supports you in mastering the M of J-U-M-P, Move Deliberately—Based on Self-knowledge."

"So if someone just changed jobs and didn't change their Operating State, they might get back into the same old schlog, just in a new location. Right?"

"That's right," said Tode, "but if they make the change inside and develop an Optimal Operating State, they can Move Deliberately, like you did when you decided to seek out the flaming orange hoop and

enter the world of humans."

"But I also chose to stay connected to the world of the marsh and to my family," said Jump, making a distinction important to him.

"You did," said Tode, "and you could, because once you got your Operating State in optimal shape, you moved deliberately beyond the belief that you had to give up the marsh in order to find the flaming orange hoop."

Limiting beliefs keep you living in a small, boxed-in existence.

They require that you put your faultfinding glasses on and insist that life be difficult and overly serious.

Through the lens of limiting beliefs, the gifts of providence are seen as mere luck.

"So could humans have both too?" asked Jump.

"Of course," said Tode. "In all areas of life–occupation, family, relationships, community service—the choices about what to do become more abundant when a person chooses while in an Optimal Operating State. For instance, let's say one of your teachers at *Lights On Institute* was unhappy at school.

She could leave and take her unhappiness with her, or she could decide to change her Operating State. Then, she might even decide to stay in the school. She might discover all kinds of possibilities she couldn't see before because she didn't know how to see the world from the inside out."

"Is that like changing her attitude?"

"It would certainly result in a change of attitude. It's different from what humans normally think of when they talk about change of attitude where the requirement that the attitude be changed is imposed from outside, by a boss or a teacher or parent. It's very important to remember that developing the Optimal Operating State is an inside job—the emphasis is on looking at the world from the inside out.

"Let's say my teacher learned about Optimal Operating State," said Jump. "How could she tell whether it was right to stay at the school or to go somewhere else?"

"If she was really dialed into her Optimal Operating State, and it was really right for her to stay, she would feel it in her bones," said Tode. "Like the feeling I have when I ride the unicycle, and the feeling you had when you first thought about attending *Lights On Institute*."

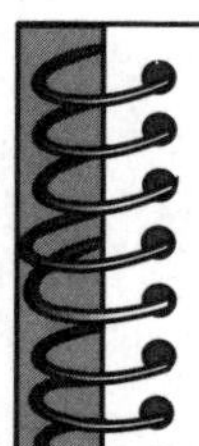

Play environments are where innovation happens.

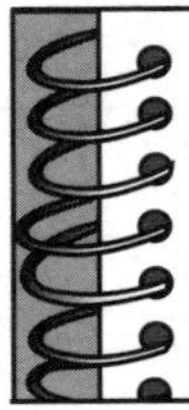

In the Optimal Operating State, play has a very deep rudder.

"Or when I'm doing my lessons on line," said Jump. "I just love it when everything's going smoothly. But it seems like that's because I'm doing something I like doing, not because I'm being in a certain way."

"That's a tricky one," said Tode. "Let's go back to the example of your teacher. If she loves to scuba dive, for example, she might think that the act of diving is what brings her joy. But she's missing a key point. You see she likes diving because when she's swimming along a reef, she naturally moves into her Optimal Operating State—without really knowing it. And because she does it without thinking, she makes the assumption that it's the diving that makes her feel great when it is really the state of mind she is bringing to diving."

"The Optimal Operating State!"

"Right."

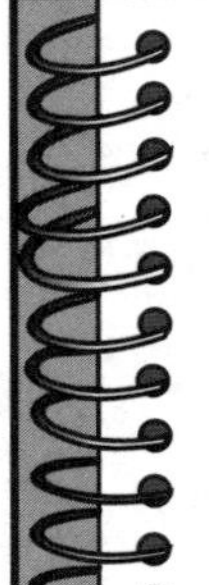

The feeling of effortlessness is not created by an external situation or event.

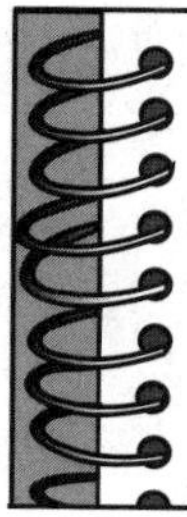

Effortlessness is created by the inner state of being, the Optimal Operating State.

"Then if she learns to create the Optimal Operating State inside herself, she can feel good no matter what she's doing. Is that it?" asked Jump.

"Well almost," answered Tode. "There's one other trick here. You see, once she knows how to live in the Optimal Operating State and experience the world from the inside out, she will make choices based on self-knowledge and the messages of The Whisperer."

"And The Whisperer could tell her to stay or to go," said Jump.

"Yes," said Tode, "but if she stays, she'll be clear about why she's staying, not just going along to get along. The result is that her life, all parts of it, will be filled with a sense of ease because she's choosing what is really right for her, and moving deliberately based on what she knows about herself."

"And that makes everything feel more like play!" said Jump, putting it all together.

"Precisely," said Tode, beaming.

"P for precisely," said Jump teasing, "and for 'Play to Win'."

"And P for passion and purpose," said Faddiest. "And it all begins with the J of Justify Nothing, because justifying everything precludes play. Sadly,

many humans won't even allow themselves to read a playful story. They stop themselves by judging it as being too childish."

"That's sad," said Jump.

Tode couldn't help noticing the profound difference between the very serious, confused tadpole he had met last spring, and the light hearted, confident young frog who now stood before him. It was a familiar change, similar to what he had seen in all of his clients as they learned to make Bold Moves based on deliberate choice. To a creature, they all exuded enthusiasm. They were aligned with their purpose in life—in their work and relationships. They were clear about what they wanted and had attained it by establishing and working a game plan. They were living, loving and working in a mood of passionate optimism underscored by hopefulness, courage, curiosity, and compassion.

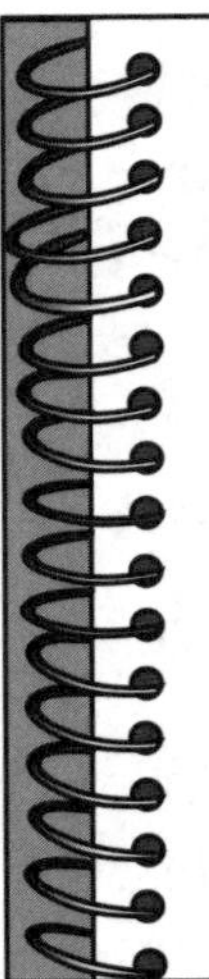

Authentic motivation occurs when passion and purpose are aligned inside you.

It's like a window opens where you can breathe the fresh air of possibility and see your way clear to act with full expression.

Life and work had the quality for Tode's clients, of being effortless. Even when it was necessary for them to exert considerable energy in performing a task, they did so in a state of ease and grace. As a result, each one, in their entirely individualized way, had a personal presence that was contagious. Other creatures wanted to be around them, to touch in some small way a life of fulfillment. Also present in each, were keen and present feelings of appreciation, prosperity, authenticity and unending openness to possibilities, abundance and joy. The daily practice these creatures had developed in learning to make Bold Moves had become the basis for healthful life habits that endured into vibrant elder years. In short, those who had been fortunate enough to find Faddiest Tode for their coach were juiced, sparked, committed, and clear.

TWENTY-FOUR

Skybox, Global Thrills Family Arena,
Kalamazoo, Michigan

Roaring engines and arena noise get louder, causing Ernest to look up from his reading. *It's the warm up act going strong*, he thinks to himself. *I've seen it all before, but there's something in the story that calls to me. Each time I have allowed myself the time to relax into Jump's world, I have gained new insights.*

Now, there are Bold Moves all around me. Evelyn is excited because she's freed herself from her doubts. Jackson is strong and confident, enjoying his Bold Move even when extreme pressure has been applied. Even Ernie reported some Bold Move action in his last e-mail. I wonder how Jump's Bold Move will work out.

He checks the remaining pages and decides to keep reading until the warm up act is over and McPlayer's performance begins.

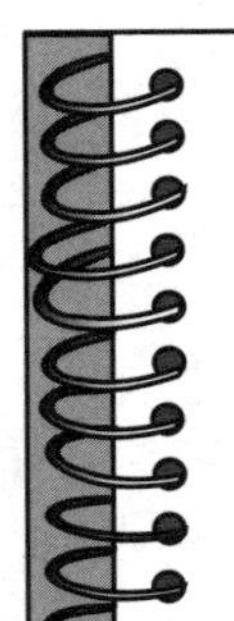

Every time you open up to the relaxed child inside of you, you find new aspects of the fully empowered adult.

The big colorful letter P stood on the marsh bank positioned perfectly to complete the word that had been forming over time, J-U-M-P. Faddiest moved to straighten out the jump rope J, as he had many times before. *Justify Nothing—Inside Yourself.* He was thinking. *There are always Critters scurrying about, forcing things out of shape. But we just keep telling them to settle down and go away. We turn down the volume and put things back into proper alignment.*

The P of J-U-M-P is directly connected to the J, because when you feel the need to justify everything, you miss out on the magic and play in life and work.

In Bold Move making, coaching and mentoring, justifying equates to the command and control methods of dictatorship. There's no room for collaboration or co-creation, so there can be no innovation.

Innovation happens in the environment of Play to Win--With Heart and Soul.

P

In the center of the curved part of the J, the young elm tree stood its ground against winter's icy countenance. Here, in the early morning, it cast a thin shadow across the big U just next door. Tracking his gaze in that direction, Faddiest recalled his unicycle ride and thought to himself, *That U carved in dirt has held up well under the eroding force of the seasons. Understand Everything—About Yourself is a continual process to keep U in shape.*

Inside the letter, was a small puddle of water covered by a sheet of ice no thicker than Saran Wrap™. *Interesting that our letter U should continue to collect water,* he thought, considering how frogs must return to the water from time to time to keep their skin soft and moist. *We all return again and again to the process of 'Understand Everything' about who we really are, staying fluid in our self-study, and fertilizing ourselves as we grow and change.* He imagined that like its shadow, the sapling's small roots had reached out toward the U, tapping a trusted source of water.

For just a moment, the chill of winter's morning penetrated the old toad's thick skin and seeped deeply into his bones. Shuddering wisely to warm him, his warts played a low, thoughtful tune and he knew his own season of change was soon coming—the big one, the final metamorphosis to complete a life full of profound changes.

The coaching sessions are coming to an end, he thought to himself. *Jump's Bold Move of entering the world of humans has served him well. He will soon move deliberately and more completely into his future life and the hours we've spent together will morph, too, into a memory—a solid, sustainable memory. The tadpole is no more. The young frog is growing wise.* Looking up, he saw the giant letter M swaying gently in the morning's frigid breeze, its moss and masking tape glistening with sun kissed frost. *M for Move Deliberately—Based on Self-knowledge.*

"No one could mistake the deliberateness of using those Mickey Mouse watches as string in our mobile," he thought. *They add weight and durability to actions that could just flap around in the wind if they weren't grounded by the time invested in building the Optimal Operating State in the J and U of J-U-M-P.* Responding to a sudden urge, he began to set and wind each of them until they built to a whimsical chorus of ticking.

While he worked, Tode reflected on his own Bold Move over the past months; cataloguing and crating his entire collection of fads and arranging for them to be donated to a small, rather odd museum on a lazy Atlanta side street. The task was nearly complete and he pondered the boxes stacked along the marsh bank that had been his home for a lifetime. *There's wisdom in these things yet,* he thought. *Bold Moves are not only about the future. There's a lot to learn from the past as well.*

He thought of all the Bold Moves that had been made as people invented and promoted things throughout the centuries. *How likely is it in the overall scheme of things that Pet Rocks would have been so popular in the 1970'? Seems like a pretty nutty idea. Yet*

salesman Gary Dahl believed in it enough to package and sell a zillion of them. And what about Dilbert? How did cartoonist Scott Adams manage to create his way out of a cubicle and launch one of the most enduring business fads of all time? Now there was a Bold Move! Glancing to the whimsical giant letter P, he mused, *Play to Win—With Heart and Soul. You can't tell me these people weren't immersed in the fun of play!*

Then he thought of all the business books that jawed on and on about how difficult it is to inspire innovation in corporations. And of a report he'd heard recently on the radio about the "great new discovery" that creativity is not supported in high stress environments. *Well duh! Creativity and innovation are connected to play, and play happens in the Optimal Operating State. High stress environments don't allow the space needed to develop an Optimal Operating State—the mental space—needed to learn to Justify Nothing, Understand Everything, and Move Deliberately. But even a small corporate cubicle can be fertile ground for Bold Moves, because it isn't the physical space that matters; it's the presence of the Optimal Operating State and the playful mood that comes with it.*

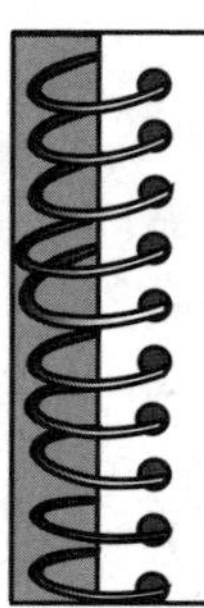

You can even make a Bold Move from inside a corporate cubicle if you've developed your Optimal Operating State.

Hearing a joyful noise, Tode smiled on seeing Jump leap into the air and land in a dramatic slide on the chilled surface of the marsh. *He sure knows how to play. If he ever works in a cubicle, he'll transform it. That's for sure. He's got a flare*! And then more pensively, he mused, *It would be fun to see what he makes of all that energy! He will be jumping, we know that, and using computers. But it seems to me there's one more piece that belongs in Jump's puzzle of fulfillment. Something with the pizzazz of that slide he just made. How will he put jumping and computer programming and flaming orange hoops together into one satisfying expression of self?*

Some components of your Bold Move will be visible to others before they will be visible to you.

Some will remain as mysteries until they reveal themselves.

Just then something happened that would prove coincidental to Tode's thoughts; a very odd gentleman appeared wearing a green waistcoat and tails. His dated outfit would have been remarkable by itself, but it was rendered downright outrageous by the fact that it was topped by an antique leather aviator's helmet and vintage goggles. The entire spectacle emerged

slowly and noisily from the brush, atop a 1909 V-twin powered motorcycle—the first of its kind made by the Harley-Davidson Motor Company.

"The name's Flatlander," said the driver, "Flatlander Museum of Fads and Collectibles."

"Ah," said Tode, "I've been expecting you."

"Did you know that William S. Harley and Arthur Davidson were barely into their twenties when they started making motorized bicycles?" asked the stranger. "Two of the greatest innovators of all times! And just whippersnappers! They started a fad of motorized bikes that has outlived fad-appeal and become not only a classic line of bikes, but a top performing business."

"That's a beauty!" said Faddiest eyeing the bike. "Displacement of 49.5 cubic inches."

"Seven horsepower!" replied Flatlander.

"Two cylinders in a 45 degree configuration," said Tode.

"You do know your classics!" said Flatlander. "Who's your friend there?"

Drawn by the noise of the Harley™, Jump drew near, staring; mouth agape at the fantastic machine. Ignoring the heat and exhaust of the thing, he reached out to touch it and was thrilled when Flatlander offered him a ride.

"We'll get down to business in a minute," Flatlander yelled to Tode over his shoulder as he lurched off looking for blacktop and a chance to put the bike through its moves for the little frog.

It's a gale force wind, thought Jump feeling cold

fury against his face. Four frog feet gripped the handlebars as the Harley maxed out moments later on a quiet country road. He yelled "With thunder!" unable to contain himself when Flatlander made the bike rev and backfire.

> Experiences that awaken passion that is in alignment with life purpose, will be felt as excitement in the mind and body.
>
> They will elicit a "wow" effect.

Jump's words were blurred against the engine's roar, but Flatlander knew well the feeling that was being expressed and realized he'd found a kindred spirit. Tode saw it too, when the Harley returned, skidding sideways with both riders whooping and hollering into a full stop, just inches short of the icy marsh water.

Well, that's that, then, old Faddiest thought to himself. *His next Bold Move is to become a HOG frog! Can't imagine how he'll manage a bike on his own, but I'd never put it past him.*

Spring lived up to its reputation for change and renewal that year in Metro Marsh. Frost gave way to slush, fostering exotic hatches of small creatures, and

myriad blossoms opened to the warmth of the sun moving northward again. Jump spent more and more time in Atlanta where he finished out his second term with honors. Moving his residence to the Flatlander Museum he earned his keep computerizing museum operations just in time to file Flatlander's tax returns on line. It was there, sleeping each night in the back room, that he first encountered the raspberry red Star Dude suit. It was printed along with the words *Justice League™ 10 Inch Action Figure 2-Pack Superman & Flash* on a collectible carton that served as his bed. The action figures themselves were said to be impossible to find. (It was Flash™, of course, whose suit was raspberry red.)

The elm sprout on the marsh bank grew bright new leaves and Old Faddiest retired to the thicket sometime in May, never to be seen again in the light of day. It is said that he eluded the grim reaper by making yet another Bold Move, and becoming a nighttime toad just for the fun of it. The last scheduled item posted in his date book read: Appointment with Plop and Croak, 3:00 am.

Ernest is pensive in the poignancy of these words. He's grown fond of old Faddiest and would like to have more of him. With just a few pages left to read, he becomes aware that McPlayer is next up in the huge arena that spreads out below the Skybox. Making the most of the intervening moments, he summarizes what he has learned about the P in J-U-M-P.

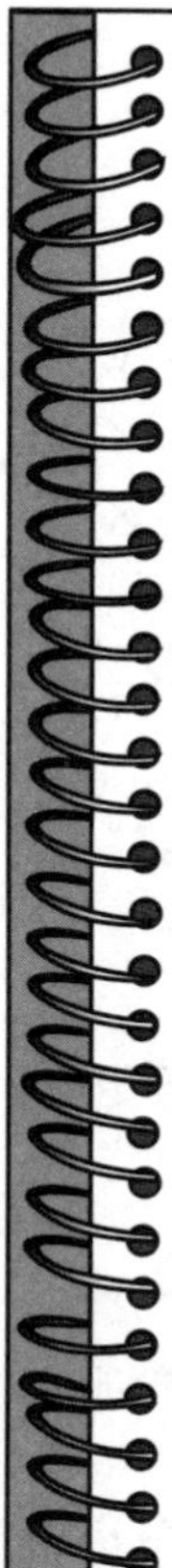

Play to Win--With Heart and Soul

Reside in a sphere where:

- Work becomes highly productive play

- Limiting beliefs like "no-pain, no gain" and "I win you lose" are discarded

True professional success equates to personal satisfaction.

TWENTY-FIVE

Center Field, Global Thrills Family Arena, Kalamazoo, Michigan

Landing hard on his custom chromed front wheel, Jackson U. McPlayer revs his Harley engine at the crowd before somersaulting onto the handlebars for his final sixty-mile an hour bow. Thirty two thousand fans roar back their appreciation for the show's finale, the famous leap through seven rings of fire. Sleek in red lycra, his muscles bulge like a gladiator.

Now he slows to make his 360 turns around the perimeter of the arena. His reflective visor recesses into the helmet, revealing the famous daredevil face. As always, his fans are delighted by this extra attention he offers before his final exit.

"Jackson, Jackson," they chant, "Jackson U. McPlayer."

But wait, he's pulling to the center of the ring. This is a new move for McPlayer! He slows. Stops. Cameras are in for a close up. We see it now on twelve huge video screens; his famous dare devil demeanor smiles through his face shield. In the stands, his fans are screaming, posturing, and flexing bodies painted in fiery rings of rainbow hues like the ones Jackson has just vaulted through. A rock rhythm keeps pace as the chant continues, "Jackson, Jackson, Jackson U. McPlayer."

The daredevil smiles broadly with obvious pleasure and a hint of mischief. He scans the arena slowly, head moving from the right to the left. Then, strangely, the head keeps turning and turning atop the shoulders, completing a full rotation until it rests again in a normal frontward position. What is this? It's like he's a big mechanical toy!

Not missing a beat, the rider raises a finger to his lips signaling the crowd into silence. Anticipation hangs densely on the promise of an explanation to come. What can this mean? What will McPlayer have to say? A drum roll rises in the stillness. Tension is cast over the giant stadium.

Jackson's broad smile opens, but in place of words, there emerges a long, elegant, iridescent tongue. Floating gracefully out like a magical ribbon, it builds speed, reaching high overhead to wrap itself around the center ring of fire—the flaming orange hoop—still ablaze from the finale. Taut to capacity, the ribbon tongue gently pulls at the image of Jackson's face until the entire image that grinned from the helmet only seconds before lifts away like a silken mask. Floating about the arena, the willowy form disappears along with the bike and rider behind a veil of colored smoke converging from all directions.

Full orchestra now—driving, eerie music—the crowd is shocked and awed as the smoke takes forever to drift away. Though blinded, the cameras are still fixed in the direction of Jackson's helmet, and thousands watch as the big screens begin to clear.

Laughter and delight bubble up in pockets as fans point and nudge, beginning to see through the haze, the image being revealed. There, inside the raspberry red star dude helmet where a head should be, is a micronized producer's console fully complimented with every imaginable computer resource known for the creation and manipulation of sounds, images, robots, and holograms—all of it being controlled by a very small green foot moving a joy stick the size of a Q-Tip™. Attached, and lounging in the producer's chair, his wart bedecked hind legs crossed and propped in a lazy pose, is a small, dewy-skinned genius, grinning this time for real and to scale.

Jackson Ulysses McPlayer is . . . . a frog! He's an amazing, Harley riding, flame jumping, and computer-savvy amphibian!

For you fans watching this from home, we can't begin to adequately describe the explosion of applause, foot stomping, chanting and general mob silliness that's . . . they've turned the cameras to the crowd now so you'll see for yourselves. Never––and we thought we'd seen it all—never have we witnessed anything like the clamor of admiration being displayed here. McPlayer has truly lived up to his name!

Inside the helmet, glancing at the live feed streaming on his tiny computer screen, Jackson Ulysses McPlayer thinks to himself, *you don't know the half of it!* And just when you think there can't be more, he strokes his keyboard instructing four laser beams to swirl around the vast arena ceiling, projecting the four-letter acronym that spells his true name:

J-U-M-P!

TWENTY-SIX

Skybox Global Thrills Family Arena, Kalamazoo, Michigan

"That is compelling entertainment!" roars Ernest to his associates. "And it's very good for business."

Modern humans, even powerful CEOs, live in a world greatly enhanced by digitally generated "virtual" reality where all manner of mythical beasts and cartoon characters freely mix with, and morph into, human beings on a regular basis. Since 1950, when Francis the talking army mule won his first award for acting in a film, talking animals have become accepted novelties on an increasingly more diverse variety of screens, from cell phones to Imax. In recent years, the facial features of actor Sean Connery were mapped and animated such that they appear as the sensitive visage of the serpent in the movie *Dragonheart*—a serpent whose voice on screen has the familiar Connery Scottish brogue. We love this stuff, love being swept away by the magic. Within this societal backdrop, Ernest's open mind has him easily accepting the idea that somehow Jackson McPlayer has found a way to talk to humans and delight them by performing as a daredevil robot. There is no shock, only awe, for Global's CEO as his attention rivets on the big screens in the arena where it has just been revealed that the Harley riding Super Dude who jumps through fiery hoops is, in fact, a frog.

The heavy skybox door flies open with a bang and Evelyn

Dodd catapults into the elite company of corporate VIPs. Ablaze with excitement, she pops the cork on a champagne bottle, toasting to Jackson's Bold Move. Regaled with handshakes and vigorous pats on the back, Evelyn is celebrated for her own Bold Move in support of Jackson.

"You've always picked winners, Evelyn," says Ernest, "but the level of risk you faced with this stunning revelation puts all of Vegas to shame." He nods and nods with a gleam in his eye that bespeaks dimensions of respect for her as yet unrevealed. "I was looking for a jumping frog, and here you are! You've been here all along, right under my nose!"

"Me a jumping frog?" she says, confused. "I think Jackson has a claim on that one!"

"We'll talk," says Ernest. "After what you and McPlayer did today, there's a lot to discuss."

A clamor of questions besieges her: Where did she find Jackson? How long has she known he's a frog? How has she kept it quiet? Where did he get his training? Is he really a computer nerd?

"Surely there must be someone behind the scenes pulling his strings!" posits one doubting Thomas.

"Not on your life," she answers. "Jackson is the most self-reliant individual I've ever met. Well, you saw earlier how stubborn he could be."

"Can he really talk to humans?" they ask.

"You heard him yourselves," she answers. "He's created a voice recognition device that translates his thoughts into the English language. He's working in secret with some technical school in Atlanta to develop versions of the thing for use with other species and other languages. Apparently he and his colleagues are gaining access to all kinds of unconventional wisdom that's been locked up in the minds of highly conventional creatures like trout and eagles. Even plants and trees."

On hearing this information, the fertile mind of Ernest Cottingham bursts open so wide that an airbus could fly through it. The implications for reviving natural systems are astounding. "When can we meet him?" he says.

The stands are still awash with gaping, fawning fans recounting, play by play, the astonishing chain of events they have just witnessed. Arena security has escorted the Star Dude and his bike to the pit, cordoning off the entire area. A thin line of VIPs snakes it's way through the milling crowd. At the head, bounds a very confident Evelyn Dodd, proudly holding aloft a wad of pit passes.

The raspberry red helmet rests, visor closed, atop the giant Harley–dude robot. Alone inside his control room, Jackson McPlayer is "taking some space." Performance exhilarates him, but his introverted nature demands that he find ample time alone in its wake to recover the Optimal Operating State he developed years ago on the banks of Metro Marsh. *I think that performance went quite well*, he muses, q*uite well indeed.*

A cushy inner layer of expanded polystyrene muffles the sound of knuckles rapping lightly on the helmet's shiny outer shell. Though it's only a dull thud, the knock signals the presence of a visitor unfamiliar with Jackson's custom doorbell. He keystrokes a command for the visor to open. As it slides from right to left, the huge, smiling eyes of Ernest Cottingham come into view at very close range.

"That was quite a surprise," the man says. "*You* are quite a surprise. I wonder if we might set an appointment to meet sometime very soon."

"Actually," Jackson says, very deliberately, as he hands Ernest his business card, "we already have a phone appointment for 8:00 o'clock tomorrow morning."

Cottingham is puzzled as he views the exotic four-color business card that shows Jackson's Harley robot in full, flaming flight.

"Turn it over," says Jackson, "and read the other side."

The next few seconds have Ernest ready to do some flaming of his own as he reads the conservative black text on the clean, white card surface:

Joseph Unger M. Putnam - Executive Coach

"Can it be?" he asks, suddenly red faced and completely flummoxed.

The exciting moment when the Super Dude came out as a frog was one thing—that was business, but this new moment of revelation, this is different. This moment is profoundly, intimately personal. Learning that a frog, A FROG, — has been coaching him—Ernest Cottingham, CEO—into a new paradigm of thinking around something called Bold Moves; this has both Ernest's mind and heart burning rubber inside, spinning out of control. *It's all fake*, says an Inner Critter finding voice in the confusion. *Everything he's told you is a sham,* says another.

Once awakened, the Critters exploit a rare opportunity to spread their virus of doubt and fear, shrink the confidence of their host, and claim his full attention. *You've been taken in,* they yell. *This whole trip, this quest for the frog ready to leap, is a joke. Bold Moves, balderdash!*

Jamming the card into his pocket, Ernest steps back a pace

and looks about, hoping no one else has noticed his sudden change of mood. *This changes everything,* spit the Critters in a slithery hissing chorus. *This s s s… is an outrage.*

Any Bold Moves coach worth his salt will immediately recognize when a client is being triggered and his Operating State is collapsing into a wave of overwhelming doubt and fear. It happens for everyone who ventures into Bold Moves territory, this defining moment, because it marks a passage into self that is essential to the making of Bold Moves—a passage which, when navigated successfully, allows for no turning back. This is the tipping point that tests the client's ability to manage the wild onslaught of Inner Critters screaming justifications for why it is just fine to cave in to disbelief, abandon one's sense of destiny, and accept the status quo—even one that will surely give way in time, to devastation. This is the pivotal choice point that asks the client to decide who will carry the microphone inside, Inner Critters or The Whisperer, that true voice of possibility, intuitive insight, and creative potential.

The degree of confusion within the client at such a moment is directly proportional to the amount of power and influence the client carries. What's more, if the Bold Move at hand is to be exceptional, and if it is to happen in the very near future, the likelihood that it can be taken out by Inner Critters is greatly magnified. That is why there are relatively few truly Bold Moves made in our world; they require a leap of faith like the one made by Indiana Jones in *The Last Crusade* when he steps off into the chasm unaware of the hidden bridge that spans it and will support him.

So here is Ernest, one of the most potent, visionary people in the world, well on his way to making a Bold Move of prime magnitude, based on values of the highest standard, driven by authentic passion and purpose. And he finds himself stopped dead in his tracks by the cloying grasp of a doubt: *A frog couldn't possibly be my coach.*

Never mind that the frog in question has just shown himself to be a phenomenal genius. Or that he's sent the entire spectator world into fits of ecstasy with his boldness of body, mind and heart. Sitting now inside the Super Dude helmet and gazing thoughtfully out at his shaken client, Joseph Unger M. Putnam is keenly in tune with the high stakes of this particular Bold Move. *If Ernest caves in, if he lets his Critters get him, if he can't access The Whisperer in this critical instant, the whole world will be the worse for it. The frogs in Metro Marsh will keep on dying and mutating, as will many others. The air from coast to coast will grow grayer, thicker, and more toxic. More fish will die. More species of all kinds will disappear from the earth. Global weather patterns will become even more unstable and the great systems created by humans will be gravely threatened—as will their creators. If a man as wise, as powerful, and as persevering as Ernest Cottingham can't find it in himself to face down doubt and fear, what chance will there ever be for someone like little Ernie, or for Evelyn, who has only touched a toe into Bold Moves country?*

Putnam's awareness of these things makes this a defining moment for him as well, but because he has seen it coming, he has already dealt with his own Critter messages. *You've really messed up by not telling Ernest who you are,* one had said as he rode his bike out of the arena moments before. Hoping to justify why Joe isn't such a great coach after all, another had scolded, *You should never have gotten into this dual role relationship with a client. How unprofessional!*

But Joe Putnam is the world's leading expert on Bold Moves. He has branded the business of Bold Moves based on the teachings of Uncle Faddiest Tode, so his relationship with The Whisperer is sturdily forged. His Critters were soon silenced by mature, constructive thoughts. *The fact that Ernest doesn't know all of who you are will give his Critters ready fuel for doubting your credibility as a coach, and that will make it difficult for you to help him when he needs you most. It's true, you've made yourself part of the problem, but you can also be part of the solution.*

Take ownership of the fact that you've been clumsy. Use your skill to support Ernest in remembering that this moment of challenge is part of his Bold Move. Hold steadily in your knowledge that what is transpiring for him is not about your identity or even your capabilities. Ernest has seen the power of Bold Moves. If he's truly ready for this next one, he will find his way. You can help by believing in his ability to reach deep down into himself and access The Whisperer regardless of the circumstances around him.

With his own Whisperer in charge of his microphone, the stage is set for what Putnam does next. He says, "That is the question of the day," in a sincere tone that Ernest recognizes without question. "Can it be?"

"Can it be—that your Bold Move coach is a frog? Can it be—that the number one daredevil, making Bold Moves in the uncertain world of humans, is also a frog? Can it be—that those two frogs are actually one and the same frog? And if by some wild stretch of the imagination those things can, in fact, be," Putnam continues, with self-scrutiny filling his voice, "how might that frog explain the fact that he has not yet informed the CEO of Global Thrills, Inc, his most respected client, of the double roles that frog has been playing today in relation to that client?"

The warmth and candor in Putnam's voice, amplified by

the translation device that makes his communication with humans possible, penetrates the confusion in Ernest's mind just enough for a clear channel to open. Happily, it is one directly linked to The Whisperer. *You've always learned good things from your coach,* it says, sounding like it is piped through a straw. *Can you get over yourself and listen to what he has to say now?*

Don't be fooled again, says a Critter. *He's not a coach. He's just a frog!*

"I imagine it's quite a shock," Putnam continues, measuring every phrase for its effect on Ernest, "finding out like this…about who I am, I mean, what I am. I've put you in an uncomfortable position. I'm sorry. I make no excuses for my choices or my behavior. I do trust, though, that you are in touch with whatever is authentically true for you in this moment. My truth is that I am a frog." Hearing himself say these words, he recalls the moment years before when he had admitted to Dermand that he had chosen to be late for jumping practice. And just as it had then, the straightforward truth eases ever so slightly, the strain on the moment.

He's right, says The Whisperer in Ernest's mind. *He's a frog, but you know your truth, remember?*

All of the phone coaching conversations Ernest has had with Joe Putnam flood into his memory: the exploration of his values as a leader and CEO; the illumination of his unique communication style; getting clear about his strengths and his challenges; owning his skills and choosing from among them, the ones to prioritize because they bring satisfaction. He recalls how amazed he was to learn about non-negotiables, and to discover that he had spontaneously defined his even before going to college. *They were like a beacon,* he is thinking, *illuminating the choices that were right for me to make.*

Thought by thought, his mind grows lighter until one of his non-negotiables explodes like a signal flare, illuminating the nature of the passage he is currently navigating*: I will make important choices and moves only when I'm in a mood of hopefulness.* His Inner Critters shrink back from the light of this affirmation and relinquish the microphone to a strong voice of possibility that says, *Putnam is a frog, yes, but a very wise frog. Re-engage with him; he has more to teach you.*

Leaning back in toward the helmet window, Ernest signals that he has found his bearings by saying with a hint of irony in his voice, "That frog obviously lives by his own set of standards––Bold Move standards that are carefully crafted from the inside out. That frog has learned the hard way that he doesn't have to justify anything because he is impeccably trustworthy both in his wisdom, and in his behavior.

"Hello, Joe Putnam, I'm delighted to meet you in person.... um, sorry, "person" is not really the right word is it?" Then, as though the terror of the prior moment has been a mere trifle, he changes the subject and magnanimously gestures toward Evelyn saying, "What do you think of this frog here? The one who's learning to jump for her own good reasons?"

"Outstanding," Putnam says, affirming both Evelyn and Ernest. "Outstanding, indeed."

TWENTY-SEVEN

Cottingham Estate,
Westwood, CA

"That was extreme, Gramps!" says Ernie, clicking off the saved version of Jackson's Bold Move. "I wish I could have been there to see it with my own eyes. Everybody went nuts when his helmet opened up all the way. Is he really Jump, the frog from the book?"

"Yes he is," says Ernest, "and to prove it, he e-mailed me a final chapter that was written only this week. Want to read it with me?"

"Sure," says Ernie, "this is so cool!"

> One leaf turned very early that fall in Metro Marsh, to brilliant gold. Working its way loose with the help of a breeze, it left the proud elm tree on the marsh bank and sailed a full thirty feet, dipping gently into a perfect landing right in the middle of a patch of blue sky that peered into its own reflection from above. Serenity is often fleeting, and so it was with that moment, for soon the leaf was scuttled aside by a frolic that arose from the depths of the marsh, reaching the surface amid great revelry.
>
> "I'll bet they couldn't believe their eyes!" said Plop.
>
> "That is so radical!" echoed Croak.

"It was a fun moment," said Jump humbly, "a fun moment."

Dermand spoke next. "I love the part where you handed Ernest Cottingham your business card with the name Joseph Unger M. Putnam on it, and he realized you'd been coaching him by phone for months. Then he ends up hiring you as a consultant to his Bold Moves initiative. It makes me so proud! My very own tadpole making a name for himself in the big time."

Jump smiled, thinking, *Dad will never relate to what I really do for a living. If he likes to think of me as a corporate consultant, why not?*

A tear formed in old Skita's eyes as she watched from under the elm where rugged roots held tight to tattered bits of a red jump rope. Delighting in her family at play, she rejoiced in their tradition of gathering together each fall. Nearby, a few rusted watchbands and scant bits of Play Doh lay as further evidence of the four Bold Move landscapes that had once graced the marsh bank, and the important work they had fostered.

Pushing himself apart from the rest, Jump floated on his back, looking at the sky and thinking, *Making a name for myself . . . J-U-M-P.*

JUMP

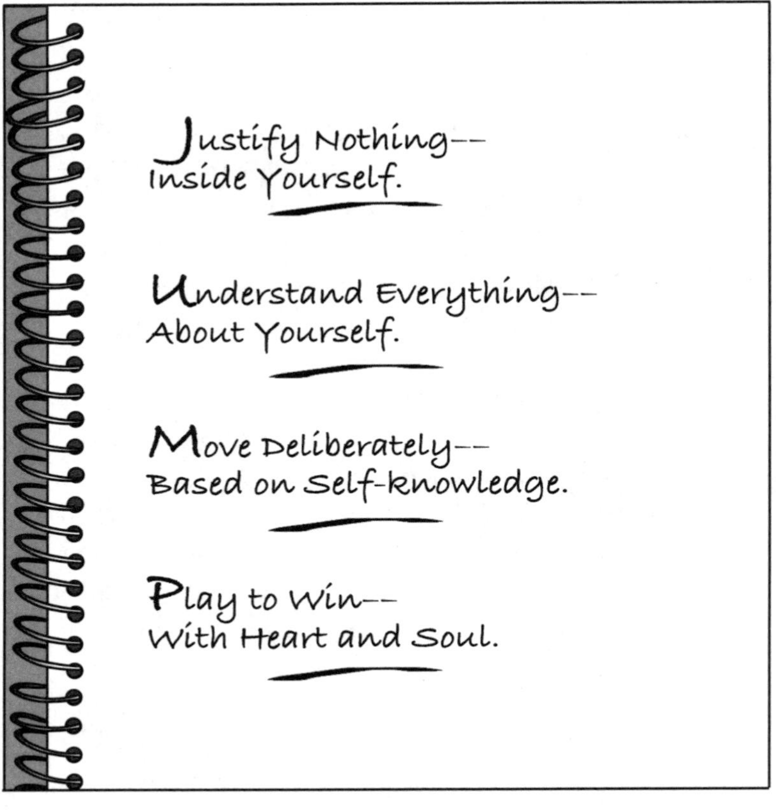

That old Tode was a wise one, a wise one indeed. Ironic though, that in the end my boldest move was simply showing my true self to the world, warts and all.

Ernie and Ernest gaze at each other in amazement, and Ernie puts words to the meaning in their faces, "How'd they do that Gramps?"

"They stayed open to possibility," says Ernest, "and they

didn't lose contact with the imaginative tadpoles they once were."

"Like you're keeping in touch with me, huh?" says Ernie.

"I suppose so," says Ernest, ruffling the boy's hair.

"Hey, I've got something to show you," says Ernie, jumping down from the sofa. Moments later he returns carrying a new papier-mâché creation—a frog sitting on a Harley.

"That is terrific!" says Ernest. "How in the heck did you make those wheels?"

"It was like making a Bold Move," says Ernie. "I thought about it carefully, like you're supposed to, then one day the idea just popped into my head to make them out of an oatmeal container. Actually, I needed two, so Mom put the extra oatmeal into a cookie jar."

"Well, you've really outdone yourself on this one. It's just great!"

"I'm thinking about entering it in the summer craft contest at the library. What do you think?" asks Ernie.

"You've got my vote," says Ernest, "but you have to make that call—that choice."

"A deliberate choice," says Ernie, "right?"

"Move deliberately based on self-knowledge," says Ernest.

"Play to win with heart and soul!" counters the boy, all smiles.

TWENTY-EIGHT

Global Thrills, Inc. Corporate Headquarters, Los Angeles, CA

Evelyn Dodd's thumb picks up a tiny smear of ink as she scans the company newsletter, fresh off the press. She's searching for signs of other Bold Move makers in her company's ranks.

Having exhibited Bold Move readiness by backing Jackson's performance in Kalamazoo, Evelyn has received direct mentoring from Ernest Cottingham for several months and now holds a position that was created specifically for her: Chief Bold Moves Officer of Global Thrills, Inc. Within just a few short years, Evelyn will grow a corporate culture at Global that fosters the making of Bold Moves at every level. As a direct result of her efforts, Global will lead its market in earnings for a decade, and benchmark corporate practices that foster sustainable social and ecological systems worldwide.

The transformative environment at Global Thrills will attract a new breed of contributors who will walk in the door knowing why they want to be there and what they have to offer. They will be trained in Bold Moves basics and encouraged to specify the ways in which their independent objectives align with those of the company. This will foster innovation in all sectors of the business: innovation that is off the chart.

Ernest Cottingham has moved to a quiet, corner office where he is able to focus more directly on those issues that will become his true legacy, the alignment of corporate values with global human values. He doesn't pretend to know what is needed by the masses of people around the globe whose lives he hopes to enhance, but he's learned how to listen very carefully to what those people have to say and combine their wisdom with his own. With these skills and many others, he will establish creative alliances wherein communities and nations can make Bold Moves of their own.

As a tribute to Joe Putnam, his Bold Moves coach (a.k.a., Jackson McPlayer, the world's hottest Hog frog) Ernest Cottingham donates the company's fleet of corporate jets to *Lights On Institute* to be used in its efforts to reverse the decline of amphibians and other endangered species on Earth. In the short span of two years, *Lights On* will garner from the DNA of these infinitely adaptable creatures the exact remedies needed to sustain them. Extrapolating from these remedies, scientists and sociologists will discover ways to balance the great systems of the earth, both natural and man-made, bringing an era of unprecedented inter-species innovation and cooperation.

Between daredevil gigs, Jackson McPlayer, d.b.a. Joe Putnam, is the Bold Moves expert of choice for corporate chiefs who understand the interconnectedness of all massive systems and are committed to building sustainable businesses in balance with the societal needs of humans and the vitality of the natural world.

POST-SCRIPT

On Tour at a Truck Stop on I-40
Flagstaff, Arizona

Jackson McPlayer hops down from the checkout counter with a bag of chips held firmly in his grip. As luck would have it, he lands on a stack of bundled newspapers lying on the floor. Through the plastic wrap that holds the bundle, he spies a headline that calls for his attention: *Cure Found for Dutch Elm Disease.*

> An effective method was found for containing a fungus that nearly drove the beautiful American elm tree to extinction during the twentieth century. Working in concert with a leading research institute in Atlanta, Georgia, arborists were able to interview two species of beetles, the native elm bark beetle and the smaller European elm bark beetle. The beetles were found cohabitating in a healthy, mature elm tree on the banks of Metro Marsh five miles outside city limits.
>
> During the interview, the beetles reported that their species had been trying for thirty years to mutate a fungicide for the parasite in question, but had been unsuccessful. Then they happened upon the tree that is now

their home and became so content living there, that they decided to produce only two generations of larvae each year instead of three. Apparently, it was larvae from the third generation of beetle that caused trees to die because they "over wintered" under the trees' bark and bored into branches in springtime, damaging trees beyond recovery.

An extraordinary new insect-to-plant-to-human communication device was used to create a three-way conversation between the scientists, the beetles, and the elm tree itself, which disclosed that it owed its good health to a bit of fertilizer placed around its seed when it was planted. The tree further claimed to have been the seed of a Bold Move––further investigation to follow.

OUR THANKS

Our combined community has been rich with resources to guide us to the writing of this important work. Special acknowledgements go to the hundreds of coaching clients whose determination to enter and live in Bold Move country provided us with key knowledge for writing this book.

To Ken Blanchard, Mark Victor Hansen, Steve Farber, Richard Whiteley, Dr. Janelle Barlow, Fernando Camino, Chris Lloyd, Bill Cleaver, Karen Kimsey House, Rick Albiero, Rob Klapper, Cynthia M. Payne, Molly Davis, and Monica Maxfield for their kind words of endorsement.

To our readers who had their red pens ready for the critical feedback that elevated the book to a more perfect product: Paula Alderson, Maggie Bafalon, Martha Ballard, Becky Breitwieser, Bill Cleaver, Tim Fincham, Tom Fulcher, Betsy and Larry Hendrickson, Vicki Javner, James Kelley, Carol Manning, Paul Miller, Diane Olberg, Rich Pinto, and Richard Whiteley.

To our seasoned practitioners who helped shape the language and brand: Mary Berry, Stephanie Rose Bird, Joanne Brem, Denise Brouillette, Beth Bruno, Don Buell, Donna Caroa, Richard Haasnoot, Carl Hammerschlag, Patty Harman, Martha Lawrence, Marsha Shenk, Vicki Sullivan, and Pat Zigarmi.

Thanks from Allan

To my Co-Founders of the International Coach Federation

Phoenix Chapter: Linda Miller, Catherine Ross, Pete Walsh and the Greater Phoenix Coaches. And to Karen and Henry Kimsey-House and Laura Whitworth for building the amazing Coaches Training Institute and being the remarkable souls you are.

To my former consulting colleagues at TMI North America and Janelle Barlow at TMI USA, who has served as a guide in a way you will never know.

To my leadership tribe, David Adams, Elena DuCharme, Phil Hart, Marci Heerman, Mariko Hingston, Trudy Kendall, Eric Kohner, Lolita Thomas, Carol Manning, Gary Minnich, Ed Morler, Mahlia Riebeling, Steve Tierney and Rita Webster for great motivation. And to Jennifer Fling forguiding us from heaven.

To my Bold Move Cheerleaders who have encouraged me along the way, Kim Austin, Katharine Halpin, Rob Haugen, Chris and Lia Huber, Nancy Paris, Marci Penman, Bill Pettit, Jeff Staggs and Leila Thorne.

And to those special souls who without them, there would be no book, the most important people in my world: my amazing wife Janis who has and will serve as my portal for the important work that I need to do; my loving daughter, Kate, who serves as a master teacher in the art of living fully. Finally to my co-author and creative muse, Shayla Roberts, for giving birth to the magical characters and co-creating the book you hold. Thank you for keeping your sage-like hands in the small of my back during my own Bold Move journey to here.

Thanks from Shayla

To the women who remind me every Tuesday how to stay deeply awake to life, Becky Breitwieser, Cookie Cimala, Bette Croce, Eveline Horelle Dailey, Gladys McGarey, Suni Paprotta, Lorean Ruggles, Doris Solbrig, Fern Steward Welch, Rose

Winter, and Barbara Wyatt.

To my Joy Associates, each an artist of the first magnitude in her own way; Rachel Blank, Arlene Friedman, Estelle Gracer, Beth Jarman, Barbara Perlman, Arlene Scult, Leah Shovers, Beth Ames Swartz, and Naomi Wagner, your support and good will have sustained me so often.

To the masters who prepared me over twenty-five years with the wisdom to translate growth concepts into processes and story: Barbara Laishley, Ph.D., Dr. Gladys McGarey, M.D., M.D.(H.), and Gloria Wallace, M.A., L.P, my prior partners in human development work; to Richard Whiteley who brought the writer in me to the fore; to George Ainsworth Land who challenged me to prove what I thought I knew about creativity and personal growth.

To my *head-in-the-clouds-feet-on-the-ground* sisters: Joanne Brem, Andrea Conlon, Fatimah Halim, Jo Norris, Judith Zaruches, and Beverlee Zell-Tamis, thank you for always stretching me! And to my business-with-heart model, Doug Reid.

To the special people who form the heart of my life: my beautiful husband Paul, my center, my grounding, my champion, my joy, and to the powerful adults who once were my children Roger, Mischa and Leslie, you have shown me more about making Bold Moves than anyone, and you've all so masterfully survived me making mine. To little Declan and Liam, I love watching your every move become bolder!

And to my remarkable partner, Allan Milham, your trust in the creative process has made our journey of co-authorship a true delight. Thank you for always walking the walk. You personify the Bold Moves message in every way. No wonder it has come to you to take into the world!

ABOUT THE AUTHORS

The creative partnership of Milham and Roberts offers punch and grace. Two visionaries in the field of human development combine their insights and sensibilities in *Bold Moves - Jump to Outstanding Self-Managed Action*. The book forms around Allan's Bold Moves principles, a strategic system for catapulting high impact individuals into lives of great contribution, both professionally and personally. Through compelling story and complementary wisdom, Shayla dramatizes the process of integrating the Bold Moves principles into daily life.

Allan Milham, MCC

Allan's *Bold Moves* technology synthesizes proprietary knowledge gained over twenty years of professional work with top performing teams and individuals in best practices cultures from start-up's to Fortune 50 companies. As a consultant for the global human capital management services firm, Drake Beam Morin, he foresaw a need to more fully align career options with client uniqueness. In leadership roles at Marriott International, he gained direct experience with the challenges of balancing corporate objectives and individual needs. In an executive role with TMI, an international human resources consulting firm, he learned critical intelligence on the dynamics of corporate culture change and human relations.

Allan's career as an executive and high impact leadership coach is distinguished. He is one of only 500 recipients worldwide of the Master Certified Coach designation awarded by the

International Coach Federation. He holds a Masters degree in Counseling Psychology from John F. Kennedy University.

Allan lives in Scottsdale, Arizona with his wife and daughter, and is an active member of his community. He co-founded the Phoenix Chapter of the International Coach Federation and holds active memberships with the National Speaker's Association and the International Coaches Federation.

Shayla Roberts

Shayla is a professional innovator creating programs, products and services that facilitate human development. As a writer, designer and personal insight coach, she combines strategic ingenuity with a unique ability to synthesize the complexities of human growth into experiential processes and simple, accessible pictures and stories. Her seminal work *Living the Gap* provides a clinical backdrop for her approach. An eighty-hour curriculum in personal transformation, it supports adults in pursuing personal transformation and whole-health, and has been tailored and instituted for use in Arizona schools as an intervention for teens at risk.

Shayla's past publications include a business fable *The Corporate Shaman*, Harper Collins, 2000, which she wrote as a ghost writer for best selling business author Richard Whiteley; and sections of *Life, Law and the Pursuit of Balance*, published by the American Bar Association 1997. She has designed jacket covers and/or illustrations for five previous human development books including illustrations for *Breakpoint and Beyond* by Beth Jarman and George Land, Harper Business Press, 1992. She created all illustrations, cover design and formatting for this book.

Shayla lives with her husband in Phoenix, Arizona where she co-facilitates twice annually, *The Phoenix Experience in Living Medicine* a week-long whole-health retreat she co-created with Dr. Gladys McGarey, the acclaimed *Mother of Holistic Medicine.*

Are You Ready For Your Next Bold Move?

For information on services and products
and to learn more about making Bold Moves,
please go to:

www.makingboldmoves.com

To contact Allan or Shayla directly, email them at:

allan@makingboldmoves.com
shayla@makingboldmoves.com

Claim Your
COMPLEMENTARY

BOLDMOVES
READINESS
INDEX

www.makingboldmoves.com/readiness.htm